Volume 2
ANIMATION

BINOCULARS

THE NEW
how it works

*This rotor of an electric motor has printed circuit
windings. The metal brush carries current from
an external source to the windings.*
Photo: Paul Brierley

THE *NEW* ILLUSTRATED
Science
and
Invention
ENCYCLOPEDIA

H. S. STUTTMAN INC. PUBLISHERS · WESTPORT, CONNECTICUT 06889

Contents

Volume 2

Published by H. S. STUTTMAN INC.
Westport, Connecticut 06889
© Marshall Cavendish Limited 1987, 1989

Animation

An animated cartoon is a motion picture created from a series of individually drawn still pictures, each one varying very slightly from the last. If these pictures are shown, one after the other very quickly, then the small differences merge into one another, and the illusion of movement is created. It is the same technique, in fact, that is used to make any moving picture – a movie film consists of a huge number of still photographs (frames), each capturing a split-second of the moving action, joined together so that they can be shown at the rate of 24 frames a second. To make an animated film, therefore, the usual technique is to use a standard movie camera to photograph the animation pictures one frame at a time, with the picture being changed between each frame. So just one minute's animation can require a staggering 1440 different drawings.

Having selected a story, the first stage of the work is to produce a storyboard. This resembles a giant comic strip and consists of rough sketches portraying the action of the story and the accompanying dialogue. Once this and the directing animator's preliminary sketches are approved by the key personnel, the storyboard, music and dialogue are recorded. The sound track is then translated on to a *track sheet* to break down the exact length of each consonant, vowel or sound; and this information is then presented on a *bar sheet* – a ruled length of paper with one division for each frame and a column apiece for character action, background movement and dialogue. At the same time, preliminary sketches and character model sheets are prepared to reveal the visual nature of the characters, color, design and general appearance of the film.

Then, a team of layout artists works with the director to set the scenes and action and produces drawings to guide the two groups of artists who do the actual animation – the background artists and the animators.

The background artists draw all the backgrounds for the film. Backgrounds include everything that will appear on the screen except the characters.

The key animators, while working within the framework of their technical instructions, are primarily responsible for the creative vitality of the film. They draw the key phases of movement – the ones that determine the life and expression of a character – while their assistants complete the in-between phases.

The background artists must work closely with the layout artists and animators because film

Left: The light path through the lenses of an optical step printer. This device – essentially a projector and a camera – is used, normally in conjunction with a computer, to create a wide range of optical effects such as the battle sequences in Star Wars. By moving the camera frame by frame images may be enlarged, reduced or flipped at will. Below: A sequence of frames from a cartoon film. It will last only about one third of a second when viewed at the standard speed of 24 fps.

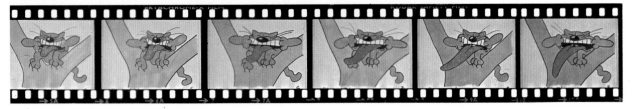

motion is achieved by both background and character movement. When a character walks, for example, it is usually the backgrounds that move while he or she walks a treadmill.

With the animation complete, the drawings are traced onto sheets of punched, clear celluloid, or *cels*, in ink (a more expensive process involves xeroxing the drawings directly from paper to cel). They are then sent to the painting department where the appropriate colors are applied to the reverse side of the cels, leaving a clean, black outline on front.

The completed cels are then sorted into scenes and sent to the camera department where they are photographed frame by frame over the proper background onto the film strip.

Computer systems are employed increasingly to speed up these laborious processes. Perhaps the simplest form of help is the computer-controlled animation, or rostrum, camera. This consists of a camera poised directly above a flat board, the camera table. The camera can be raised or lowered in a precise series of tiny steps; the table can also be moved back and forth, or rotated.

Normally, the cameraman follows a precise sequence of camera or table movements to achieve the effect of pans, zooms or cartoon movements. For example, a cartoon figure might be photographed in a sequence of running movements. To add realism, a background *cel* is moved backwards in precisely calculated steps so that the cartoon figure appears to be moving forwards during a sequence.

By allowing a computer to operate the rostrum, a far more precise sequence of movement can be achieved. The result is labor-saving, and gives smoother, more realistic, motion. The device has also opened up the field for complex special effects – which have been used in feature films such as Star Wars, Superman and their sequels.

Computers are used in animation, however, to do much more complex work – including the actual drawing and animation. But before a computer can work on or store a picture, it has to be translated into computer language. To do this, the image is broken up into a mosaic of tiny squares of tone. Each square or PIXEL (picture element) is then assigned a number that represents its tone level. Thus the artist's drawing becomes, for the benefit of the computer, a string of numbers.

See also: Computer; Computer graphics; Lens; Memory device; Microchip; Movie camera; Optics; Soundtrack; Television techniques; Video camera; Video recording.

Right: Flair is a system of computer-generated graphics which can be used to create a cartoon. The artist draws the image on an electronically sensitive tablet with a stylus which can be commanded to represent anything from a fine pen and a wide brush to an electronic air brush. The screen image consists of 576 television lines, each of which is broken down into 768 pixels (the smallest accessible unit – or picture element). Each pixel can be colored with any one of 256 combinations of red, green and blue output signals. The 8085A micro-processor allocates an 8-bit number to each pixel allowing pictures to be manipulated and stored.

Antenna

An antenna is a device for transmitting or receiving radio waves. Antennas may be tiny – as in miniature transistor radios – or massive dishes such as tropospheric scatter antennas.

A transmitting antenna converts the electrical signals from a transmitter into an ELECTROMAGNETIC WAVE (a wave of electric energy), which spreads out from it. A receiving antenna intercepts this wave and converts it back into electrical signals that can be decoded and amplified by a receiver, such as a radio or television set. A radio transmitter produces its signal in the form of an alternating electric current, that is, one which oscillates rapidly.

Electromagnetic waves

The oscillating current in the transmitting antenna produces an electromagnetic wave around it, which spreads out from it like the ripples in a pond. This wave sets up electric and magnetic fields. The lines of the electric field run along the antenna and those of the magnetic field around it. Both the electric and magnetic fields oscillate in time with the current.

Wherever this wave comes into contact with a receiving antenna, it induces a small electric current in it, which alternates back and forth along

Three important component parts of a satellite/cable television system. The satellite signal is received by the large dish (below left) then sent up to 40 miles (60 km) across country from a microwave tower (below center) to the viewer's rooftop UHF antenna (right). The signal may then need to be amplified.

Below: In order to prevent unauthorized users from viewing, satellite TV signals can be encoded and system subscribers provided with electronic decoders. Television sets not fitted with a decoder receive a meaningless image. The transmission encoding may be modified as desired.

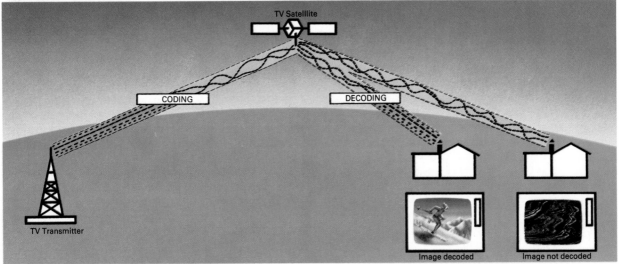

Above: A fitter adjusting a microwave dish antenna.
Above right: The trans-horizon station at Mormond Hill, Scotland provides oil platforms, 200 miles (320 km) offshore, with direct worldwide links.

the antenna in time with the oscillations of the wave. Although this current is much weaker than the one in the transmitting antenna, it can be picked up and amplified by the radio.

The air is full of radio waves at all frequencies, which the antenna picks up indiscriminately. Each radio or television set has a *tuner* with which the desired frequencies can be selected.

Each frequency is associated with a wavelength. This is because the waves, as they radiate out from the antenna at a certain frequency traveling at the speed of light, space themselves a certain constant distance apart. The higher the frequency, the shorter the wavelength (the product of the two being always equal to the speed of light). A transmission with a frequency of 1000 kHz has a wavelength of 984 ft (300 m).

Electrical waves travel along a wire at a similar speed. It will therefore greatly increase the efficiency of an antenna if its length is correctly related to the wavelength of the signal it receives or transmits – ideally one half or one quarter of the wavelength it receives or transmits.

Receiving antennas inside domestic radios cannot be even one quarter as long as the wavelength, and in any case have to work over a wide range of wavelengths. But fortunately, the signal from a public broadcasting transmitter is so powerful that it can be received on an inefficient antenna.

Types of antenna

The same principles apply to transmitting and receiving antennas. The simplest form of antenna is a single elevated wire with an earth connection. This type of antenna was introduced in the early days of radio by Guglielmo Marconi, who found that by using a wire instead of a small metal cylinder as he had done previously, he increased the range of his transmitter from one hundred yards (one hundred meters) to two miles (three kilometers).

This type of single element antenna is called a *monopole*. It is connected to only one terminal of the transmitter; the other terminal is connected to earth. This arrangement does not stop the current flowing in the antenna; it streams between the antenna and the ground as if across a CAPACITOR, and sets up an electromagnetic field between the two. The ground here is said to be used as a *counterpoise*. Automobile radio antennas use the vehicle body.

Antennas called *dipoles* are also used. These consist of two rods of equal length (again half- or quarter-wave) set end to end a few inches apart. One rod is connected to each terminal of the transmitter, but they are not connected to each other. The field forms about both rods, linking them. No grounding is needed, since the rods counterpoise each other; they are said to be *balanced-fed*.

Directivity

Antennas radiate or receive better in some directions than others and are said to possess *directivity* (sensitivity to the signal angle).

The directivity of an antenna is very clearly illustrated in the comparatively inefficient internal antennas of portable radios. These may be of two types: the *loop antenna*, a length of wire wound many times around the the interior of the cabinet, and the *ferrite rod* antenna, where the wire is wound around a magnetic material which increases its efficiency. For the best reception, the plane of the loop, or a plane at right angles to the ferrite rod, should pass through the transmitted signal.

Reception of a broadcast is often impaired by interference from another transmitter with nearly the same frequency. Medium and long wave radio signals follow the curve of the Earth and can travel hundreds, or even thousands of miles with comparatively little loss of strength, which means that they can cause serious overcrowding problems.

The shorter wavelengths of very high and ultrahigh frequency transmissions (VHF and UHF), which are used for hi-fi radio and television broadcasts, tend to travel in straight lines, and so reception stops shortly beyond the horizon. This means that there has to be a large number of VHF and UHF transmitters to cover a country, which can cause re-

ception problems to someone halfway between two transmitters sending different programs.

Both problems can be solved by using a strongly directional receiving antenna lined up with the desired transmitter. The classic type of highly directional antenna is a domestic television antenna.

This consists of a half-wave dipole antenna – the part of the UHF band used in many countries for color television has wavelengths ranging from 25 in. (64 cm) down to 13 in. (35 cm). The dipole is lined up with the transmitter. In front of it (as seen from the transmitter) there is a row of *directors*, which are plain metal rods approximately the same length as the dipole, but not electrically connected to it or the set. Behind it is a reflector, which is similar in appearance but at right angles to it.

The directors and reflectors pick up the signal. This causes a slight current to flow in them, so that they re-radiate the signal, though very weakly and with a changed phase – positive for negative. As a result the reflected waves coincide exactly with the direct waves so reinforcing the received signal.

See also: Electromagnetic radiation; Electronics; Microwave; Radio; Satellite.

Below: Antennas radiate both an electric field – red/blue – and a magnetic field – green/brown.

TRANSMISSION AND RECEPTION

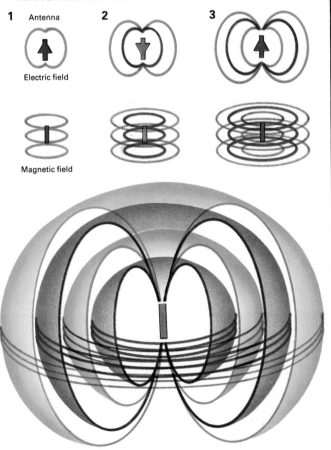

1   Antenna

Electric field

Magnetic field

2

3

• FACT FILE •

- In the not too distant future most TV programs will go out via Direct Broadcasting Satellite (DBS). The satellites will receive signals from the ground station, and retransmit a signal, up to 100 times the strength of current satellite transmissions, to the consumer terminals. The "homesat" dish antenna can then be as small as 2 ft (60 cm) in diameter.

- An alternative technology radio receiver designed for use in Third World countries consists of a cheap speaker, a six-inch nail, a fringe of short copper wires, and a fruit-juice can. Sufficient power to pick up a single frequency local signal is provided by burning wood chips or dried animal dung in the top of the can.

- Project Seafarer is the U.S. Navy's answer to the problem of communicating with submarines traveling fast and at great depth, in the possible event of calling for a retaliatory nuclear strike. Extra Low Frequency (ELF) waves would be transmitted using a grid of antennas, each up to 60 miles (96 km) long.

Antiaircraft gun

Antiaircraft (AA) guns were first used in World War I when they were adapted from equipment designed for other roles. Their job was to prevent enemy aircraft flying at such a height that they could observe, photograph, range artillery, bomb with accuracy or attack troops at low level; and they had to prevent hostile aircraft from flying in formation which allowed them to use the power of their combined defensive armament against counter-attacking aircraft. These requirements persisted until the end of World War II, by which time the great speed of jet aircraft made AA gunnery impractical against high flying targets.

The AA problem

This may be summarized as the time of flight: while the AA shell, which is set on an unalterable ballistic trajectory once it has left the gun muzzle, travels upwards towards the target aircraft, that target is itself traveling through the sky. For a guided missile, which can change course and maneuver as it homes in on its target, this travel distance is not of ultimate importance but it can affect a shell's accuracy very considerably. For example, a target traveling at the now modest speed of 200 mph

Above: An Oerkilon 20 mm twin antiaircraft gun on the British Navy's auxiliary H.M.S. Fort Grange.
Below: A U.S. Navy 40 mm automatic gun capable of firing 160 rounds per minute over 11,000 yards.

(320 km/h) would travel almost 1¾ miles (2.8 km) during the 30 second flight of a 3.7 in. AA shell. The position of the target is known at the moment the gun fires but once the shell starts on its way no further control can be exercised over it, and so certain assumptions must be made about the behavior of the target during the time of flight of the projectile to meet it. These assumptions are that the target will maintain a constant course, height and

speed shortly before and during the flight of the shell or, if any of these are changing, it will be at a constant rate. The higher and faster the aircraft is flying, the longer the time of flight of the shell and the less likely are the assumptions to be justified.

The apparatus developed to pinpoint the future position of the target is called a predictor. Although extremely complex in design, it is simple in principle. The predictor follows the path of the target

PHALANX WEAPON SYSTEM

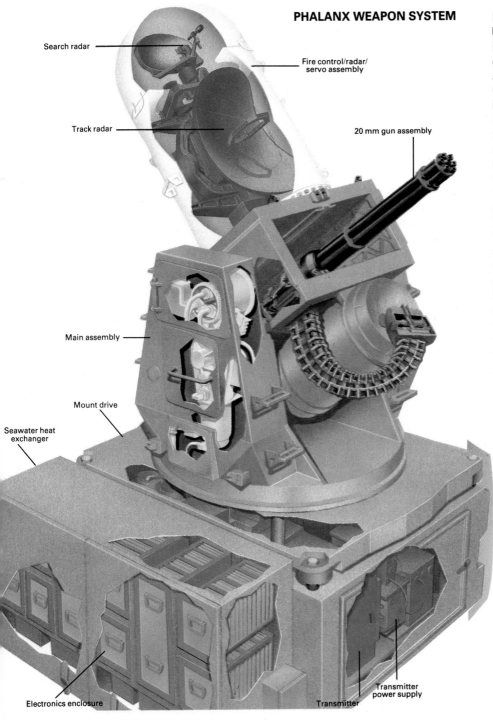

Search radar

Fire control/radar/servo assembly

Track radar

20 mm gun assembly

Main assembly

Mount drive

Seawater heat exchanger

Electronics enclosure

Transmitter

Transmitter power supply

Left: Fleet defence for U.S. carrier battle groups is based on a triple zone counter to conventional and nuclear attack. Currently, the emphasis is on last ditch close-in protection. This requires the defensive system to detect an offensive aircraft or missile no closer than 2000 yards from the ship and destroy it before it gets within 100 yards. There are two options: gun or missile systems. The gun solution is exemplified by the Navy's Phalanx system. Designed by General Dynamics, it is the Navy's first all-weather, automatically-controlled close-in antiaircraft and antimissile gun. It uses radar to direct the six-barrel Gatling type 20 mm gun toward the target. With a firing rate of 3000 rounds per minute, the gun effectively produces a screen of high density, depleted uranium-cored lead projectiles, practically guaranteeing a successful hit.

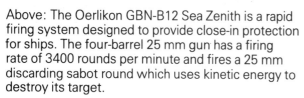

Above: The Oerlikon GBN-B12 Sea Zenith is a rapid firing system designed to provide close-in protection for ships. The four-barrel 25 mm gun has a firing rate of 3400 rounds per minute and fires a 25 mm discarding sabot round which uses kinetic energy to destroy its target.

and measures the bearing (direction) and elevation. The change in bearing and elevation in a short period of time enables the course and speed to be calculated and this, with the height supplied by a modified range finder, gives all the target data. Initially an optical range finder was employed, but this could not be used at night and later was replaced by radar. The trajectory of the shell depends on its initial velocity, the retardation due to its shape and diameter, its weight and stability in flight, together with the meteorological conditions at various altitudes through which it passes. All these factors are fed into the predictor.

The business of prediction is now carried out by computer with data processing techniques so fast that it can deal with attack by the fastest low-flying jets. In the U.S. Vulcan Air Defence System, the Vulcan 20 mm Gatling gun (which can spew out bursts of fire at a staggering 3000 rounds a minute) uses a computer to offset the optical sight to allow for the distance covered by the target while the shells are on their way to it. The computer gains its information from a range finding radar and the movement of the gun as it tracks the target with the gunner using optical sights. Because air attack is made at such speed that unaided target analysis is impossible the Vulcan is designed to be used as part of a larger system in which early warning radar will give notice of approaching aircraft and IFF (Interro-

Top: The West German Gepard is an antiaircraft variant of the Leopard tank. It is armed with twin Oerlikon Contraves 35 mm guns.
Above: The control unit of the British Aerospace Blindfire Rapier – a radar-controlled missile system. for use against low flying aircraft.

gation Friend or Foe) radar will recognize signals emitted by friendly aircraft. This will relieve the gunner of the problem of identifying aircraft as hostile or not in the split second available to him.

The Vulcan's sheer weight of fire gives it a high probability of hitting the target but, for guns that fire at a slower rate or for some missiles, the probability of achieving a kill is increased by a PROXIMITY FUZE system that detonates the warhead in the target area. The proximity fuze works by using a radio device built into the shell, to detect when it is near the target. The strength of the signal determines when the fuze should detonate the shell.

Antiaircraft missiles

Although the guided missile is preeminent in the modern antiaircraft arsenal – particularly against distant or high-flying targets – the gun has not been discarded. Both the U.S. and the U.S.S.R. use radar informed gun systems and the British, who had switched to all missile defence, were rudely shocked during the Falklands War. During the battle to secure their landing the British pressed Bofors guns firing a slow 120 rounds of 40 mm a minute into action and used them with open sights together with every machine gun that could be found an AA mounting. There is no evidence that these unguided guns secured a kill but the Argentines' 35 mm radar controlled guns brought down a Royal Navy Sea Harrier – an outstandingly agile aircraft.

Despite this, the more deadly AA weapons in the Falklands and all modern wars are guided missiles. There are a variety of ways of guiding SAMs (Surface to Air Missiles) to their targets. The simplest are those contained within the missile itself and therefore impossible to jam by using electronic counter measures to disorientate the guidance system. In this category are the infrared or heat-seeking weapons that home in on aircraft exhausts. This sort of guidance is very popular in the lightest, most portable SAMs such as the U.S. Stinger. The heat-seeking sensor indicates the direction of the target and the missile's on-board control system alters its flight path accordingly either by turning its wings or by deflecting the thrust of its rocket motor by blanking off one of its exhaust nozzles.

In more complicated guidance systems the missile can be made to change direction in response

Above: The Dutch-built 30 mm Goalkeeper anti-missile system effectively forms a wall of lead.

Right: The Roland SAM (surface-to-air missile), is designed to protect fast-moving armored columns. Widely used throughout NATO countries, the system is carried on tracked vehicles. Typical of most SAMs, both Roland I and Roland II employ radar for target acquisition and IFF (Identification Friend or Foe). Roland I has an infrared guidance system that is optically aimed by the operator and steered automatically along the line of sight. Roland II is guided by tracking radar, although it can also be sighted optically in the face of radar jamming techniques.

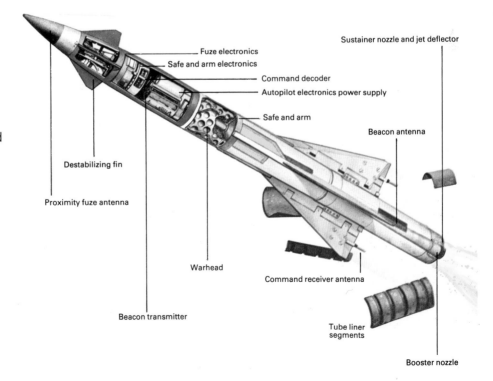

Fuze electronics
Safe and arm electronics
Sustainer nozzle and jet deflector
Command decoder
Autopilot electronics power supply
Safe and arm
Beacon antenna
Destabilizing fin
Proximity fuze antenna
Warhead
Command receiver antenna
Beacon transmitter
Tube liner segments
Booster nozzle

to radio command generated by control systems responding to information from radar, laser or TV camera. Radar can be used simply to illuminate the target so that the missile's homing device picks up the radar signals reflected off the hostile aircraft. Radar illumination is another system in which control is carried on board the missile but radio commands are needed in radar command guidance which employs two radars: one radar tracks the target and another tracks the missile, and their information is fed into a computer which causes signals to be transmitted to the missile so that it will intercept the target.

Only one radar is needed for beam riding guidance. This stays locked onto the target and the missile rides down the beam until it strikes. LASER beams can be used as an alternative to radar if the target is within sight of the controller. Radar has an advantage at night or at distance but the laser designation is impossible to jam or deflect with counter measures. In the same way TV cameras can be substituted for radar sets in a command guidance system in difficult radar conditions. TV systems are frequently used against low level air attacks on ships because radar finds it difficult to detect targets against the background sea clutter.

The hostile aircraft is not a passive target for guidance systems. It frequently carries sensors that indicate to its pilot when it has been picked up by radar. At this point counter measures can be activated to discharge chaff to clutter the radar or to transmit radio signals that will confuse missile guidance. The aircraft can also drop flares to deceive heat-seeking missiles and maneuver violently.

See also: Bazooka; Laser and maser; Radar.

Above: The Rapier antiaircraft missile system provides an ideal defense against surprise attack.

Below: A twin-barrel 3in. 50 radar controlled anti-aircraft gun on board a U.S. Navy troop carrier.

Antifouling techniques

Antifouling techniques are used to keep ships' hulls, and other such objects submerged in the sea, free from a build-up of aquatic animals and vegetation. Unchecked, infestation greatly decreases the speed of a ship and requires additional fuel to compensate for the resulting loss in performance. Other financial burdens of marine fouling include the cost of docking, loss of earnings and the physical cleaning of the vessel.

The organisms which settle on ships' hulls disturb the smooth flow of water and cause an increase in the drag factor of about 0.25 per cent in temperate waters. After six months, an afflicted ship's top speed may be reduced by up to 2 knots, and about 40 per cent more fuel may be used in maintaining the cruising speed.

The most common fouling species are barnacles and green algae, but in some regions tubeworms, hydroids, sea squirts, mussels and various red and brown algae also give trouble.

The most efficient means of achieving protection is with antifouling paints. These contain *toxicants* – chemicals that are poisonous to fouling organisms. Cuprous oxide is the most common agent, but it is often boosted with other compounds such as tributyl tin oxide. In order to be effective in combating the organisms, the toxicants have to dissolve out of the paint into the surrounding water.

Types of coating

There are two types of antifouling paint: the first type has a base material (the *matrix*) which is insoluble in water, and the second has a matrix which is slightly soluble. Included in the former are materials such as vinyls, and in the latter the acidic resin known as *rosin*.

The soluble matrix coatings, being slightly acidic, react with the seawater, releasing the toxicant slowly. With paints of the insoluble kind, new layers of cuprous oxide particles are exposed to the seawater as the outer ones dissolve; the matrix itself remains in place. There are also coatings which rely on mechanical erosion, caused by the flow of water over the surface, to expose the toxicant which then dissolves in the water.

Traditionally, it was held that the average time between defoulings was six to nine months. Applied properly, present day antifouling paints can give protection for two and a half to three years.

War experience

In a war, fouling can be a crucial factor. It has been calculated that the struggle for control of the Pacific islands during World War II was shortened by as much as 18 months because Japanese antifouling techniques lagged behind those of the United States. Japanese ships had to return to port for defouling every nine months and it was expected that American ships would have to do the same. On several occasions the Japanese attacked targets, expecting U.S. guard ships to be safely in dry dock when in fact they were not, and as a consequence the attackers sustained heavy losses.

At present, attention is being paid to developing improved antifouling paints, more effective toxicants, alternative methods of distributing these compounds, and methods which do not require the use of toxicants at all. In the latter case, research is attempting to find repellent compounds.

See also: Corrosion; Metal; Ship; Warship.

Left: The red cuprous oxide used in antifouling paint contrasts vividly with the incrustation of barnacles and algae on untreated steel.
Below: Underwater cleaning with a high pressure hose – the surest and most economical method.

Antimatter

Antimatter, if it existed anywhere in the universe, would be composed exclusively of ANTIPARTICLES. Each of the building blocks of common matter, such as the ELECTRON, PROTON and NEUTRON, has its own antiparticle – a sort of mirror image of itself. On contact a particle and its antiparticle annihilate each other in a flash of pure energy.

The existence of antimatter was originally proposed by the English physicist, Paul Dirac. In 1928 he developed a theory of the electron, the lightest particle in nature, by marrying Einstein's theory of special relativity and the new theory of quantum mechanics which described the world of the atom. To his surprise Dirac found that his theory predicted a new particle in addition to the familiar negatively charged electron; a particle with identical mass but opposite charge.

Four years later Carl Anderson of the California Institute of Technology detected Dirac's positive electron. This first antiparticle was named the POSITRON. It wasn't until 1957 that physicists at the University of California discovered the next antiparticle, the ANTIPROTON – the negatively charged counterpart of the positive proton.

Physicists now know that all particles have associated antiparticles although a few, such as the

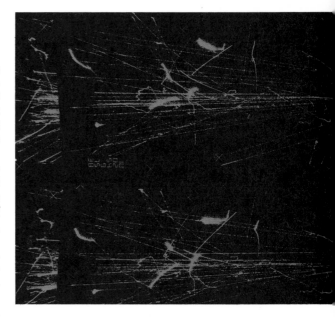

Above: Two views of a head-on collision between protons and antiprotons showing the tracks of the shower of particles produced by the impact. The beam of antiprotons (below) is formed by bombarding a metal target with high-energy protons. The particles produced, including the antiprotons, are separated by a magnetic field and guided to the site of the collision.

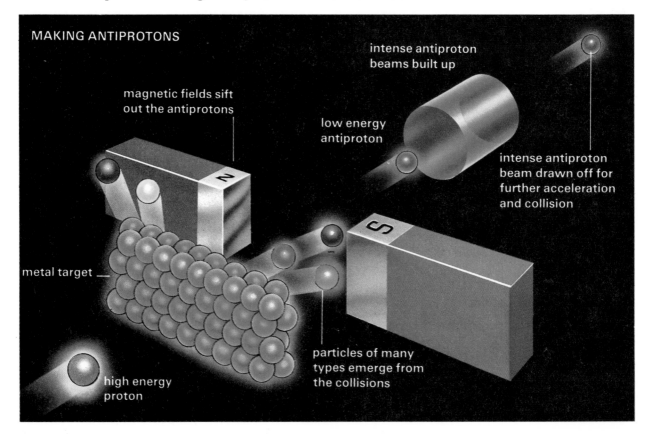

MAKING ANTIPROTONS

intense antiproton beams built up

magnetic fields sift out the antiprotons

low energy antiproton

intense antiproton beam drawn off for further acceleration and collision

metal target

particles of many types emerge from the collisions

high energy proton

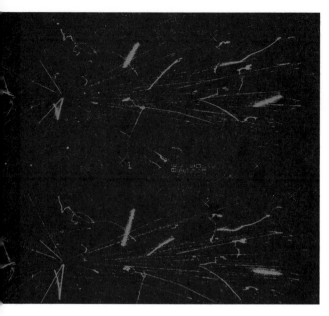

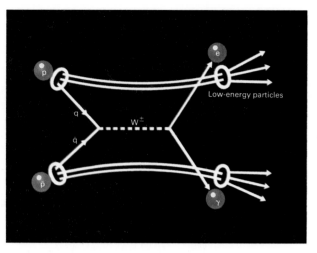

Above: Subatomic particles, quark and antiquark, produce a little known particle called a W boson which was first observed in January 1983 after experimenters at CERN (Center for European Nuclear Research) ran millions of high-energy tests. An enormous amount of energy is needed to release a W and it is only recently that equipment large enough to do this has been available.

PHOTON – the particle of light – are their own antiparticle.

According to Einstein, matter can be created out of energy since mass and energy are the same thing. But, when a particle is created in this way it is always accompanied by its antiparticle. For example, an electron and a positron can pop into existence when a high energy photon, or gamma ray, gives up its energy. This process is called PAIR PRODUCTION. In the reverse process a particle and its antiparticle are just as radically transformed in a burst of gamma rays.

The universe seems to be made largely of matter. If this were not so and there were antistars or anti-galaxies – giant collections of antistars – then occasionally matter and antimatter would come into contact and a violent explosion would result. But astronomers, who have explored much of the universe with their telescopes, have never observed this phenomenon.

As particles and antiparticles are created together it is a great mystery that our universe is made of matter and not antimatter, or even a mixture of the two. Some physicists now suspect that in the BIG BANG, the titanic explosion in which the universe was born fifteen billion years ago, matter and antimatter were not created in equal amounts. The laws of physics may be slightly lop-sided, favoring matter, and they may have allowed the creation of a slight excess of particles over antiparticles. When annihilation had run its course one particle in every thousand million was left over. This would neatly explain why there are today, about a thousand million remnant photons for every particle of matter in the universe.

See also: Matter; Particle accelerator.

Above: Complex machinery, over 1 mile in diameter, is buried deep underground for collision experiments at CERN. Huge caverns at different levels hold the equipment which will detect and record every possible aspect of the particles and movements. Thus, an experiment studied 200 ft (60 m) underground will also be monitored for additional data in a cavern 75 ft (23 m) below ground.

Aqualung

The development of the aqualung has led to the growth of diving as a sport throughout the world. More importantly, though, the aqualung is invaluable in offshore oil and gas operations, marine engineering and search-and-rescue work.

The aqualung or SCUBA (Self-Contained Underwater Breathing Apparatus) is a life support system which supplies air to a diver, without the need for safety lines to the surface or for cumbersome protective bells.

Essentially, the aqualung consists of three main units: a demand valve, a cylinder filled with compressed air and a harness. Two important functions of the demand valve are to provide air only on demand (when the diver inhales) and to exhaust exhaled air, but its vital role is to regulate the pressure of air supplied to the diver. Typically, the cylinder is pressurized to 2800 psi (200 bar) – more than sufficient to explode the lungs and entire chest cavity if applied to the respiratory tract, which is accustomed to breathe at only 14.5 psi (1 bar).

Moreover, the deeper the diver descends, the greater is the pressure due to the weight of the water above. At 30 ft (10 m), the water exerts a pressure of 29 psi (2 bar), and 14.5 psi (1 bar) for every additional 30 ft (10 m) of depth. The body consists largely of solids and liquids which, unlike air,

are virtually incompressible, even under great pressures. It also contains air filled cavities – the lungs, sinuses, inner ear and stomach – all of which connect with the respiratory system. If the air being inhaled is not at the same pressure as the water around the body, these cavities are forced to contract. Even at shallow depths, the contraction can compress the air, making breathing extremely difficult. In fact – at sufficient depths, the pressure crushes the cavities flat and kills the diver. The demand valve regulates the supply pressure from the cylinder and matches it with the pressure at the various depths to which the diver descends without the need for manual adjustment.

The demand valve

In its simplest form, the demand valve is a circular box consisting of two chambers, each separated by a flexible diaphragm. One chamber is open to the sea, so the diaphragm is at the same pressure as the surrounding water. The other chamber is connected to the diver's mouth by a flexible tube. Inside the second chamber is a tilt valve, which seals off the high pressure air supply from the cylinder. When the diver inhales, the pressure in the second chamber is reduced, and the diaphragm is pushed in by the water pressure so it presses on the tilt valve. By making the diaphragm large, the tilt valve lever long and the high pressure valve seat small, the small pressure change is amplified to open the high

Left: The modern Aqualung is a development of the sports equipment used by swimmers just before World War II. The first self-contained system, freeing the diver from the air hose and surface pump, was designed by an Englishman, H. A. Fleuss, in 1878. The rebreather suit, in which the exhaled gases were circulated through a container of chemicals to scrub out the carbon dioxide, formed the basis of self-contained suits from the turn of the nineteenth century until 1943. Then, Emil Gagnan, a French engineer, developed a fully automatic valve for Jacques Cousteau.

Right: The first stage of a piston type demand valve (top) serves to reduce the pressure of the charged air cylinder from 2800 to 108 psi (200 to 7½ bar). The second stage of the demand valve (below) incorporates the diver's mouthpiece. Both the diaphragm and the exhaust valve are made from soft, flexible silicone. During exhalation the valve spring holds the valve shut and spent air is exhausted through the rubber sealed valve at the side. When the diver breathes in, a slight suction is created in the injector tube causing the inlet valve to open and thus provide air *on demand*. The first stage of the demand valve is attached to the top of the compressed air cylinder and is joined by a flexible tube to the second stage.

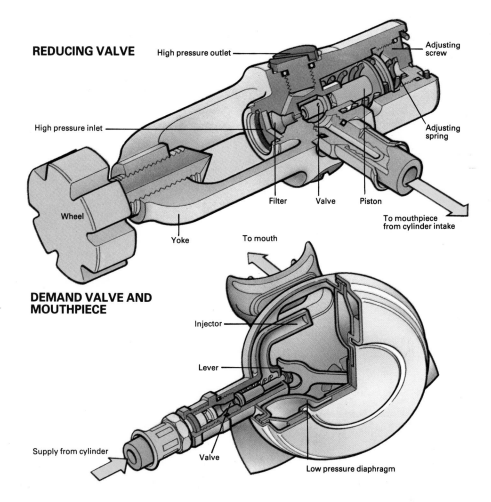

REDUCING VALVE — High pressure outlet — Adjusting screw — High pressure inlet — Filter — Valve — Piston — Adjusting spring — To mouthpiece from cylinder intake — Wheel — Yoke

DEMAND VALVE AND MOUTHPIECE — To mouth — Injector — Lever — Supply from cylinder — Valve — Low pressure diaphragm

pressure valve against the pressure of the spring.

As the tilt valve opens, high pressure air rushes into the second chamber, raising the pressure and pushing the diaphragm back until the pressure in both chambers is the same as the water pressure. The tilt valve closes and no more air enters until the diver inhales again or descends with the valve. Exhaled air is vented into the first chamber to balance the unit.

This type of valve is called a single stage valve, but it is more usual to reduce the cylinder pressure in two stages to provide smoother air flow. The first stage is on the cylinder and the second forms part of the mouthpiece. Some demand valves can be connected to a low pressure air supply from a large cylinder or compressor at the surface, enabling the diver to stay submerged for long periods.

The cylinder
The cylinders containing the air supply are deceptively simple. They are made from steel or aluminum and are strictly controlled in manufacture and maintenance to ensure that they are safe to use. The development of a reliable high pressure cylinder has enabled divers to carry sufficient compressed air, which is healthier to breathe than pure oxygen which becomes toxic at depths greater than about 30 ft (10 m). A 23 in. (600 mm) long cylinder having a diameter of 7 in. (175 mm) might contain about 1.7 mm³ of air, compressed at a pressure of around 2800 psi (200 bar). On the surface, this air should last an adult about 100 minutes; at a depth of 30 ft (10 m), it lasts about 50 minutes and at 90 ft (30 m) about 25 minutes.

Birth of the aqualung
The aqualung is a refinement of various diving equipment that had remained relatively unchanged for nearly 100 years, until just prior to World War II. At about this time swimmers started using the new goggles, fins and snorkels in the Mediterranean for sport fishing and fun. Among them was a young naval gunner, Jacques Cousteau. In 1943, a French engineer, Emil Gagnan, developed a fully automatic demand valve for Cousteau, and the modern aqualung was effectively born.

See also: Diving suit; Pressure; Submersible.

Archaeological technology

Archaeology has undergone a scientific revolution. Traditionally, the procedures of archaeology have involved excavating sites, uncovering artifacts – products of workmanship – and establishing a chronology or time scale against which the artifacts can be dated. These procedures are still important, but they are being supplemented by techniques and instruments from a wide range of sciences.

A reliable chronology can be provided by scientific dating methods. By analyzing the composition of artifacts, the raw materials from which they were made can be ascertained – essential in understanding ancient trade and technology. Zoology and botany are applied to give insights into the environment of our ancestors, and to show how they utilized the plants and animals of their time.

Discovery of sites

Aerial photography has revealed many new archaeological sites. An earthwork, plowed so that it is difficult to recognize at ground level, can be seen from the air when the sun is at a low angle and the slight ridges and hollows are clearly revealed by their long shadows. Some sites are totally invisible from the ground but, under suitable conditions of climate and crop growth, may be seen from the air by means of *crop marks*. Buried pits and ditches filled with good topsoil retain moisture well, so vegetation above grows taller and greener, whereas buried roads and walls provide a well-drained infertile subsoil which tends to stunt crop growth. When plowed furrows cut into archaeological features, such as ditches or walls, the topsoil may become colored by materials brought up from below, so that the site shows as a *soil mark*.

Before excavation, it is necessary to pinpoint archaeological features on the ground, and a number of instruments have been developed specifically for this purpose. Resistivity meters are used to measure the RESISTANCE of the soil to the passage of an electric current. Electricity is conducted by water in the ground which contains dissolved mineral salts. Well drained soils retain less moisture, so they have a greater electrical resistance than less drained ones. Since buried archaeological features retain moisture to differing degrees, they can be detected by their contrasting electrical resistance.

Right: One of the 17 human mummies given radiological examinations in 1975 at Manchester Royal Infirmary, Britain. They were X rayed at night or weekends to avoid alarming patients using the same facility. Four different methods have been used: Fluoroscopy, orbital radiology, tomography, and xerography. It is also possible to study the soft tissues by the application of paleopathology by first rehydrating the mummy tissue with a 5 per cent formal saline solution. Sectioned tissues can then be examined under an electron microscope. The investigations revealed evidence of osteo-arthritis, sand pneumoconiosis, pericarditis, pleurisy, and arteriosclerosis.

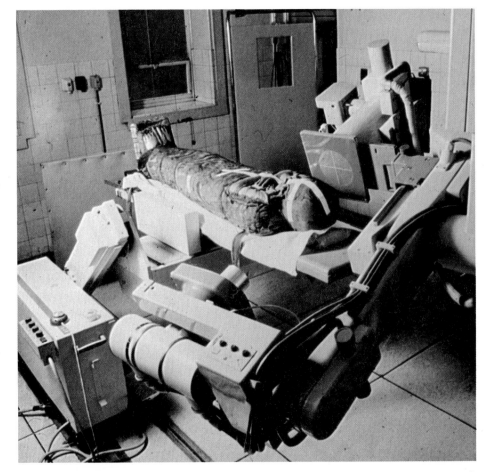

Top: 1981 excavations at a Ptolemaic settlement at Saqqara. Nearby, three huge temples were exposed. Above: Remains from a Predynastic burial, before 3100 BC, found at Gebelein cemetery, Upper Egypt.

Above: Ancient ditches discovered beneath Georgian buildings in Bath, Britain, by means of a portable proton magnetometer – a device which can detect where top soil has sifted into different strata.

In carrying out a resistivity survey, four iron rods are inserted at equal intervals into the ground in a straight line. An alternating electric current is passed through the two end rods while the resistance is assessed by means of a meter connected to the inner two. The rods are moved across the field in a series of parallel traverses to record variations.

The proton magnetometer has been developed to measure minute variations in magnetism. Measurements of this type can be a rapid means of detecting archaeological features on sites that are not magnetically disturbed by electric pylons or the underlying bedrock. Most soils and rocks contain a scatter of minute particles of iron oxide, each of which has a weak magnetic field. The fields are oriented randomly and tend to cancel one another. If the raw material in which they are embedded is heated above about 1292° F (700° C), the particles lose their magnetism, but on cooling they become remagnetized in the direction of the Earth's field.

The particles will now reinforce one another's magnetism so that the net magnetic field of the material is greatly increased. For this reason, kilns and hearths can be readily detected by the stronger magnetic effect at their site.

Metal detectors are of considerably less value in archaeology than is commonly believed. If an excavation is properly conducted, metal artifacts can be recovered in the normal manner, and valuable information about a site can be lost completely by digging small holes and removing objects from their proper archaeological context.

Dating methods

The invention of RADIOCARBON DATING has had a profound effect on archaeological chronologies. Small quantities of the radioactive ISOTOPE CARBON-14 are formed in the upper atmosphere when the nitrogen in the air is bombarded by cosmic rays. The newly formed isotope, contained in the gas carbon dioxide, is distributed throughout the Earth's atmosphere, taken up by plants and passed to the animal kingdom in food. All living matter contains minute quantities of carbon-14 supplied constantly from the reservoir in the upper atmosphere. On death, the supply is not renewed and the quantity of carbon-14 diminishes gradually at a constant rate as the unstable isotope decays back to nitrogen. Consequently, the amount of carbon-14 in a sample of wood or bone is a measure of the sample's age.

All the isotopes of an element are chemically identical, so it is difficult to separate carbon-14 from other carbon isotopes, but the amount can be estimated by measuring the radioactivity of the sample. This is usually done by converting the carbon in the material to a gas, such as methane (CH_4), and measuring its radioactivity with a sensitive GEIGER COUNTER shielded from atmospheric radiation by a thick armor of metal. Another method is to convert the carbon of the sample to the liquid benzene (C_6H_6) and measure its radioactivity with a *scintillation counter*, another kind of particle detector. With knowledge of the present-day radioactivity of the sample, the radioactivity that the sample would have had originally and the decay rate (half life) of carbon-14, the date of death of the organism, from which the sample came can be calculated accurately.

In the early development of the method, the original radioactivity was estimated by assuming that the amount of carbon-14 in the atmosphere, and hence in living matter, had remained constant over the past few thousand years, but by taking measurements of carbon-14 in trees, this assumption has been shown to be false. Trees grow by adding a fresh ring of wood to the circumference annually. In a growth year, the ring is broad, whereas in a bad year, it is narrow. In the U.S., a tree ring series has been built up for the past 7000 years, using the long lived bristlecone pine tree, and study of the carbon-14 content of individual dated rings has shown that there must have been significant variations in the carbon-14 content of the Earth's atmosphere – enough to cause serious errors in the calculated date.

Thermoluminescent dating, first demonstrated at Oxford in 1968, is proving valuable in assessing the age of fired materials, such as pottery. Radioactive particles given off by the decay of the isotope found in any crystalline substance tend to knock off electrons from the atoms of which the substance is

Above: A specialist laboratory which makes it possible to date organic remains by their carbon-14 content even though only tiny quantities are created each year. Below left: Radioactive elements decay at a fixed rate characteristic of the element involved. Half the content in an organic sample will decay in a certain time, then half of what is left in the same time again. Below right: The fixed decay rate of carbon-14 provides the means by which artifacts such as this carving from a Viking ship may be dated with a great deal of accuracy.

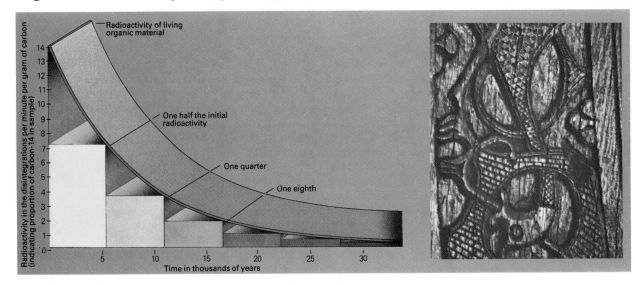

Right: Pottery may be dated through the phenomenon of the changing magnetic pole over time. When pottery is fired, the iron oxide particles in the clay become oriented with regard to the magnetic pole. This orientation can then be used to relate the pottery artifact to the known magnetic pole at any particular date against the apparent pole positions from the national archeomagnetic data file.

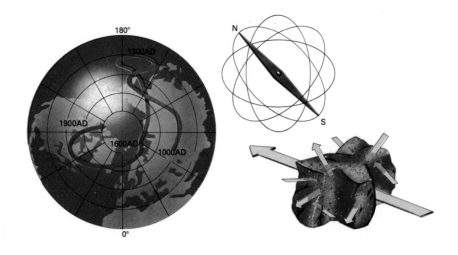

Left: Two pictures showing the contors of the famed Hadrian's wall and forts, across Britain. Oblique sunlight reveals more to the aerial camera than the eye on the ground can discern. The infrared photographs show crop marks that indicate where Roman field ditches, trackways and enclosures were placed.

made. Some of these electrons become trapped in imperfections in the crystal structure.

When the crystalline matter is heated, the electrons are released and energy is given off in the form of light. The intensity of the glow is related to the age of the crystal or to the time that has elapsed since the material was heated by ancient people – each period of heating drives off the geologically accumulated glow and the buildup begins again. Particles of quartz are present in almost all ceramics, and these quartz crystals are commonly used in dating.

Artifact analysis

Microscopes are often used to study the composition of artifacts. By examining thin, transparent slices of stone implements, the rock from which they are made can be determined. By comparing the details of mineralogy and texture with samples from present day rocks, scientists can often determine precisely the region from which the original rock came. In Britain, a long program of research on axes from the late Stone Age has demonstrated remarkable

countrywide transportation during the early period. The rock and mineral composition of pottery can be examined in the same way. Interesting results have been obtained in both western Britain and in New Mexico, where certain groups of prehistoric pottery, previously assumed to be of local manufacture, had clearly traveled considerable distances.

Chemical analysis of artifacts is usually done by optical emission SPECTROSCOPY. A small sample is burnt between carbon rods carrying an electric current, the light is separated by prisms and the resulting spectrum photographed. The position of dark lines on the photographic plate indicates what chemical elements are present and in what quantities. This has made it possible to distinguish groups of artifacts with similar compositions and hence, quite probably, similar origins.

Outstanding success has been achieved with *obsidian*, a natural volcanic glass which was used in many parts of the world for the manufacture of sharp stone implements. Obsidian occurs in only a few locations, and research in the eastern Mediterranean has shown that each outcrop has its own

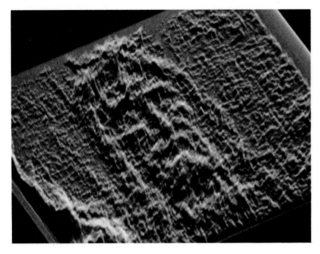

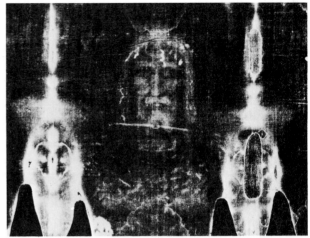

Above: Scientists working on the Shroud of Turin made this relief image of the face with a VP-8 image analyzer using hidden 3-D information.
Right: One of the Shroud's greatest mysteries is the fact that a photographic negative produces a superior image to that of the actual cloth.

characteristic content of minor elements. Finds from archaeological sites can be assigned to their parent outcrop after analysis and a picture emerges showing when different sources were exploited and how products were traded.

Optical emission spectroscopy is increasingly being replaced by *neutron activation analysis*, which can be nondestructive and more accurate. A small sample is subjected to a flow of neutrons in an atomic reactor, converting many of the elements present to their radioactive isotopes. These decay, producing a characteristic radiation, and by analyzing the gamma rays given off it is possible to assess accurately many of the elements present.

Environment
The study of biological remains from archaeological sites does not usually require elaborate equipment. A sample of soil can be agitated in water, using a flotation machine. Small seeds, charcoal fragments, bones, snails and insect remains float to the surface. These can give information about diet, vegetation and climate.

Pollen is extremely resistant and is often well preserved in lake muds, heathland soils and particularly in peat bogs. These are important because they contain a pollen record of vegetational, and hence climatic, changes that have taken place in the region while the bog was forming. Pollen is extracted by destroying other organic and mineral matter with strong acids then collected as a residue and examined under a microscope.

See also: Carbon; Isotope; Spectroscopy; X ray.

• FACT FILE •

- A computer analysis of the possible astronomical alignments of the stones at Stonehenge revealed that twelve alignments pointed to maximum positions of the sun in 1500 BC, the estimated average time of construction, while twelve pointed to maximum positions of the moon. The alignments were accurate to about 1 degree, and the mathematical odds against these results occurring by accident are ten million to one.

- Amino acid racemization is the technique now being used to date bones too old for conventional radio-carbon techniques, i.e. over 35,000 years old. By gauging the rate at which certain amino acids, held in disequilibrium during life, proceed to balance up after death, a date for death can be estimated. Using this method humanoid bones from the shores of Lake Ndutu in Africa have been shown to be up to 600,000 years old, while Paleo-Indian skeletons in California indicate migrations at least 40,000 years ago, although traditionally it has been considered that the first population of the New World immigrated between ten and fifteen thousand years ago.

- X rays of Egyptian mummies too fragile to be unwrapped have shown that the families of the Pharoahs suffered from such bone diseases as arthritis, poliomyelitis, and curvature of the spine. The X rays have also revealed jewelry hidden beneath wrappings and layers of resin.

Armor

Armor was historically a defensive covering for the body but, with the coming of vehicles and their increasing use by the military, armor has become recognized more commonly as a protective covering for vehicles. The development of body armor was closely and quite naturally interlinked with the development of weapons.

The first known use of armor is shown in the wall carvings of Assyria dating from about 3000 BC. It took the form of a simple helmet, probably made of leather. By 2000 BC the soldier had *scale armor*, a leather or fabric cloak covered with overlapping small plates of bronze or iron. The Greeks, with their more advanced metallurgy, were able to fashion large bronze plates to cover the body.

The Roman legionary used several forms of armor including *mail*, the earliest known examples of which appear to date from around the third century BC. Mail was composed of a series of metal rings each interlocking with four others. During the Middle Ages the skill of the armorer improved and soon the entire body was protected by mail. As new, stronger weapons were developed to pierce the mail, extra protection was obtained by the fitting of metal plates at the most vulnerable points. The first evidence for these plates appears in the mid-thirteenth century when reinforcing pieces are shown fitted at the knee, a part always difficult to protect with mail and, on a horserider, particularly vulnerable. By the end of the fourteenth century the entire body was protected by *plate armor*.

During the fifteenth century, in Germany and Austria, the armorers made a type of armor known as *Gothic*. It was characterized by a graceful shape with the edges cut in cusps and trimmed with brass, and is among the most attractive of all armors.

Below: An armored truck is most at risk from attack when it is loading or unloading, because the crew is working outside. On the move, the truck can withstand a military-style assault.

Towards the end of the fifteenth century and early in the sixteenth century, German armorers developed a style known as *Maximilian*. This is easily recognized, since the surface of all pieces, except the greaves, were fluted to give extra strength and good glancing surfaces. The helmet enclosed the head and was known as a *close helm*.

Firearms were becoming more common in the sixteenth century and the bullets from these crude weapons were able to penetrate most plates. Some thicker armor was made to withstand the bullet but many troops began to discard it as being rather superfluous. Instead, they wore cheap, mass produced munition armors and a few wore heavier armor with long thigh pieces reaching to the knees; this style is usually known as *cuirassier's* armor. Mail continued to be widely used as a secondary defence until the seventeenth century.

By the end of the seventeenth century the majority of European troops had discarded all armor and only a few cavalry units still retained their cuirasses, and in the eighteenth century even these were

Far left: A football uniform is a good example of armor that protects without hindering the wearer. Left: An aircrew's armor gives protection from crash as well as gunfire.
Below left: The driver of this armored car survived to identify the would-be assassin. The toughened glass is laminated to prevent fragmentation, and the body panels are lined with Kevlar, a light synthetic material.

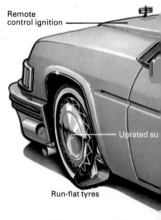

Remote control ignition

Uprated su

Run-flat tyres

Hidden smoke and CS gas cani

PERSONAL PROTECTION — THE SECURITY BLANKET

finally abandoned as firearms were adopted.

During the nineteenth century armor was almost totally discarded and few thought that it would ever return. In the Orient, however, armor continued in use much longer. Indian, Persian and Turkish warriors wore defences composed of mail and plates. Japanese armor differed in that it was made of small, lacquered metal plates laced together.

Modern armor

During World War I troops in the trenches suffered a high proportion of head wounds. From 1915 onwards most armies began to issue some form of head protection known variously as a tin hat or a steel helmet. Other armor in the form of thick fabric and metal cuirasses (back and breast plates) and helmets for machine gunners, snipers and others liable to suffer dangerous exposure were also used. When tanks were introduced in 1915/16 there was an interesting reintroduction of mail — tank crews were issued with a face mask. This consisted of a metal plate covering the eyes, cheeks and nose while the mouth and chin were protected by a short curtain of mail.

These face guards protected crewmen from the *bullet splash* which could immobilize early tanks if they came under sustained machine gun fire. Although the bullets could not pierce the armor they could knock spots of metal off its interior or, where they met a joint between armor plates, their nickel jackets were ripped off but their molten lead cores squeezed between the interstices. This made the inside of a tank under fire a hail of tiny metal fragments that were unpleasant if rarely lethal.

By World War II improved metallurgy had made bullet splash a thing of the past. As tanks came under attack from weapons using ever increasing velocities to build KINETIC ENERGY, their armor was developed to meet the threat. At the time most effort went into increasing armor thickness as far as possible before the tank suffered a lack of agility that would degrade its combat performance. Care was also taken to present a sloping surface that might cause an antitank round to ricochet off harmlessly – so the turrets and glacis of tanks were curved and shaped appropriately.

Since World War II even more ingenuity was developed to meet a more varied antitank threat. New materials such as titanium made armor ever more resistant to penetration and points of weakness were ironed out as entire turrets were cast rather than welded. Despite this, tank armor

Below: A modern armored car fit for a president or monarch can shield its occupants from even the most determined terrorist attack.

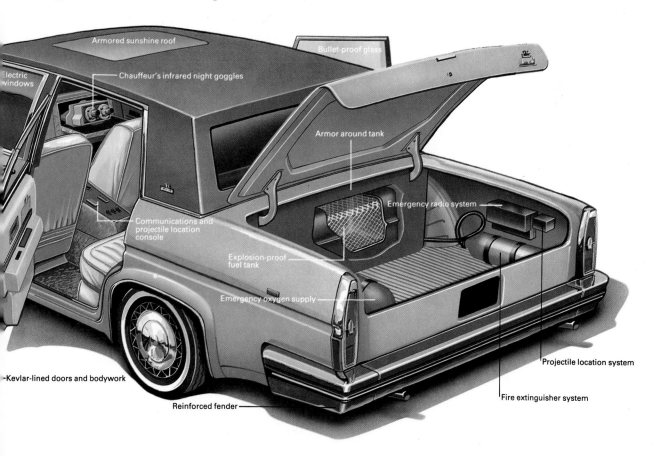

- Armored sunshine roof
- Bullet-proof glass
- Electric windows
- Chauffeur's infrared night goggles
- Armor around tank
- Emergency radio system
- Communications and projectile location console
- Explosion-proof fuel tank
- Emergency oxygen supply
- Kevlar-lined doors and bodywork
- Reinforced fender
- Projectile location system
- Fire extinguisher system

Plastic shields and bullet-proof clothes are part of the armory of a modern French riot squad.

became less and less of a protection as shaped high explosive warheads using chemical energy proliferated on the battlefield. During the 1960s the Soviet Union developed spaced armor which could withstand attacks from HEAT warheads designed to set up vibrations that would detach a large and lethal scab from the armored vehicle's interior wall. The Soviets' T-64 and T-72 tanks which entered service in the seventies had two skins of armor so a scab detached from the outer skin could be kept out of the tank by the inner skin.

By the mid seventies the British had developed laminated Chobham armor which is used in most modern NATO Main Battle Tanks including the powerful U.S. M1. Chobham armor is layered in a series of titanium, nylon and granular material thicknesses. The titanium provides the traditional unyielding hardness of armor to attack but the nylon manages to absorb immense penetrative power by yielding a fraction and the granular material diffuses the direct explosive power of shaped chemical energy charges of all types. By using Chobham it is believed that the front and sides of the U.S. M1 Abrams are absolutely invul-

nerable to chemical energy attack and highly resistant to kinetic energy attack.

Modern body armor

The weight, shape and thickness of this latest composite armor means that it is not necessarily suitable for all armored fighting vehicles so its use is restricted to Main Battle Tanks. However infantry have increasingly come to have personal armor available to protect them as well as armored vehicles. In World War II bomber crews in particular began to use *Flak jackets* which were padded jackets containing steel, aluminum or glass fiber plates combined with heavy nylon textiles. These garments were often enough to keep out shrapnel or low velocity bullets and they have been increasingly used by fighting men in Korea, Vietnam and Northern Ireland.

In the last decade there has been a great improvement in the quality of this modern body armor. The old idea of having an armor of impenetrable hardness – usually of steel – still survives and new materials have been brought into service. Steel plate is probably still the most effective body armor and the only type likely to resist high velocity rounds. Modern tempering and quenching processes can produce a light, low-alloy steel that is cumbersome but not hopelessly unwieldy when made into a bullet-proof garment. Ceramics and reinforced plastics are lighter but bulkier and are not as resistant to penetration as steel – particularly from automatic weapons which can secure a number of hits in a very close cluster on a target.

The main discovery in improving modern body armor has been in the area of using heavy-weave nylon cloth. Layers of heavy weave cloth are simply impenetrable to low velocity bullets so that their noses mushroom or flatten on impact. Sixteen layers of heavy weave nylon will keep out all standard handgun bullets and twenty four layers will defeat magnum sizes. This makes nylon very useful for police work in societies where handguns are common but, because a suitable garment retains bodyheat, it is uncomfortable to wear for lengthy periods.

Personal armor has been taken as far as it can go today in the Explosive Ordnance Disposal (EOD) suit worn by bomb disposal experts. A typical suit would weigh 48 lbs (22 kg) and can be fitted with a cooling system. Even this elaborate clothing would not offer protection against large explosive devices and it is, in any case, almost impossible to offer great protection to hands and fingers without compromising an operative's dexterity.

See also: Ammunition; Armor-piercing shell; Bazooka; Bullet; Explosive; Gun; Kevlar; Metal; Missile; Plastics; Tank; Textiles; Warship.

Armor-piercing shell

Every advance in the design of tank armor is soon followed by improvements to the ammunition used to attack them. Even armor 10 in. (250 mm) thick is no protection against modern antitank shells.

The invention of the ironclad warship led to the first types of armor-piercing shell, for coast defense and naval use, but it was the arrival of the tank which led to improved designs. Early weapons, such as the World War I Mauser antitank rifle, which fired a steel bullet capable of penetrating 1.1 in. (28 mm) of armor from a distance of 150 ft (45 m), and the 2-pounder (pr), 6-pr and 17-pr antitank guns used in World War II, were all of the same type. They achieved their effect by punching a hole in the armor, relying on their mass and velocity for penetrating power. This attack is called the *kinetic energy* (KE) attack.

Kinetic energy is expressed by the formula $E_k = \frac{1}{2} mv^2$, where E_k is energy, m is the mass of the moving body and v its velocity. Kinetic energy is proportional to the mass of the shell, but also proportional to the velocity squared. This means that doubling the mass of the shell doubles the kinetic energy, but doubling the velocity increases the energy by four times. Designers are thus concerned primarily with increasing the velocity at which a projectile hits the armor.

To obtain the maximum effect, the kinetic energy should be applied to the smallest possible area of the target. This is achieved with a long, thin projectile, which can have a large mass and move at high velocities. The long, thin, heavy projectile is ideally suited to maintain its velocity as it passes through

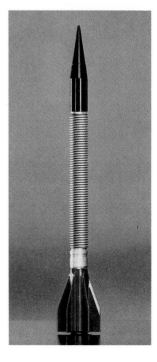

Far left: A 105 mm kinetic-energy round designed to penetrate armor at ranges up to 1640 ft (500 m). The charge is packed in a brass cartridge case with primer and granular propellant, and the projectile sits on top. The projectile (center) comprises a three-segment sabot with a driving band and screw thread, and the subprojectile or penetrator (left) made from standard tungsten alloy (STA).
Above: 15 ft (4.5 m) after firing the sabot breaks away from the tungsten projectile.

the air, but inside a gun the maximum muzzle velocity is achieved by having the largest possible diameter shell which will give the largest base area on which the gas pressure can act. So there is a contradiction in requirement – maximum diameter inside the barrel, minimum diameter while the shell travels through the air and strikes the target.

This contradiction was resolved by the British invention of the *armor piercing discarding sabot* (APDS) shell, which was first tried in the 6-pr and subsequently the 17-pr gun. It has since been used on the 20-pr, 105-mm and 120-mm tank guns.

In the APDS shell, there is a small diameter central core made of tungsten carbide, which is a strong and heavy material. The core is surrounded by a light magnesium alloy sleeve, or sabot, which produces a large diameter when the shell is loaded. When the propellant is ignited, a pressure of more than ½ ton per square inch is applied to the large cross-sectional area of the core and sabot. The pressure gives the shell a large acceleration so that it emerges from the muzzle at about 4460 ft/s (1360 m/s). The force of the explosion breaks up the sabot into sections, but the confinement of the barrel holds it together until it reaches the muzzle. The

sabot then separates from the core which proceeds towards the target. At impact, there is a large kinetic energy contained in a small diameter solid shot, which produces an extremely effective attack on armor plating.

In the 1970s, the *fin stabilized discarding sabot* (FSDS) projectile was developed for use in smoothbore tank guns. This has a long, dart like subprojectile of either tungsten or of depleted uranium (uranium containing less of the isotope U-235 than it normally does), with fins to stabilize it in flight. It is carried in a light metal sabot similar to the APDS shot, and functions in the same way. The additional length gained by using fin stabilization increases the mass and thus the kinetic energy imparted to the target. Armor-piercing FSDS rounds are in use with NATO and Warsaw Pact armies.

Unfortunately, all kinetic energy projectiles need a large and heavy gun, which although acceptable in a tank, cannot be managed by infantry who in battle have to maneuver the weapons into and out

Below: APDS shells are designed to disable tanks by piercing their armor, but HEAT and HESH rounds shock off scabs from inside the tank.

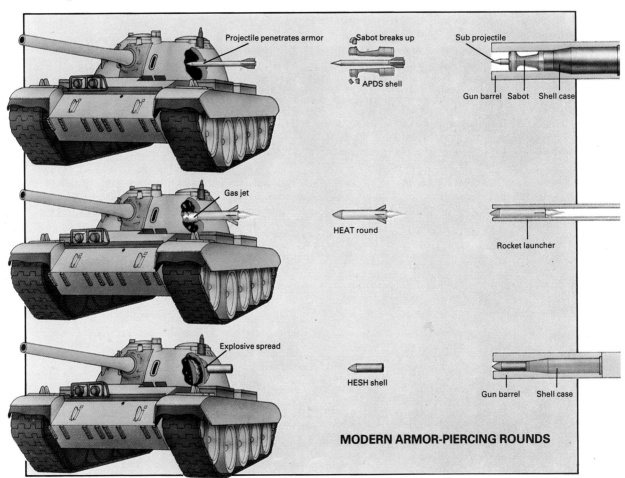

Projectile penetrates armor

Sabot breaks up

Sub projectile

APDS shell

Gun barrel Sabot Shell case

Gas jet

HEAT round

Rocket launcher

Explosive spread

HESH shell

Gun barrel Shell case

MODERN ARMOR-PIERCING ROUNDS

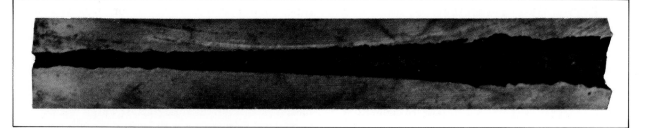

Above: A hole blasted, from left to right, through 15 in. (400 mm) armored steel by an 80 mm HEAT warhead. A sensor in the nose of the warhead detonates the charge while it is some distance from the target. The explosion produces a jet of gas and molten metal which bores through the steel. Left: A recoilless rifle, the 48 mm Carl Gustav, fires a shaped-charge round, which is deadly at close range.

of action. To meet the need for a lightweight launcher, methods of attacking armor other than by kinetic energy were developed. Some other form of energy had to be employed, and the solution was found in chemical energy (CE) produced by the detonation of a high explosive (HE) charge in a shell. By this is meant not the explosion produced by a conventional HE shell, which relies on blast and fragmentation, but a specifically designed shell utilizing the controlled application of CE. The first CE shell was based on the *hollow charge*, or *shaped charge*, principle and is known as the *high explosive antitank* (HEAT) round. The front face of the HE filling is hollowed out to produce a cone. A liner of copper or aluminum is placed in front of the cone.

When the shell hits the tank, the high explosive is detonated and the energy produced is focused into a parallel sided gaseous jet – like light from a parabolic reflector. The jet, and the now molten liner carried with it, has a velocity of about 18,000 ft/s (5500 m/s). Together, the jet and liner weigh only a few pounds, but the high velocity produces a high kinetic energy, which forces the charge into the armor to a depth of about three times the diameter of the cone. A modern 84-mm recoilless antitank gun can penetrate 10 in. (250 mm) of armor plate at a range of about 3200 ft (1000 m).

The effectiveness of the HEAT round is judged not only by its ability to penetrate the armor but also by the energy of the jet, liner and fragments of armor plate, which pass through the hole into the interior of the tank to kill the occupants, cause fires and destroy equipment. Unlike the kinetic energy round, the effectiveness of the HEAT round is independent of its striking velocity, so a low velocity launcher carried by a single infantryman can be a highly effective antiarmor weapon. Today, one-shot throwaway antitank rocket launchers firing HEAT rounds are used by most NATO countries.

An alternative method of using CE is known as HESH – *high explosive squash head*. In this type of round, a large quantity of plastic HE is carried in a shell. When it strikes the armor plate, the HE filling spreads out on the armor face, and is detonated by a base fuze. This system does not penetrate the plate. Instead, it relies on the shock wave from the detonation which is transmitted to the tank interior. When the wave reaches the far side, it is reflected, overstressing the metal on the inside of the plate so that a large scab, often two-thirds of a meter across, is detached. This whirls around inside the tank at high velocity causing casualties and damage.

To produce a large scab on a modern tank, a caliber of about 4.5 in. (120 mm) is required. Some countries – including the U.S.S.R. – use another method known as HEAP *(high explosive armor piercing)* to defeat armor. In this, the kinetic energy method is used to penetrate the plate and then an HE charge is detonated once it is through.

It is doubtful if the effective range of the high velocity gun can be extended substantially. In any event, the widespread use of guided missiles with long range and pinpoint accuracy has made further development unnecessary. Missiles cannot use the kinetic energy effect, so they carry HESH in the largest sizes and HEAT in the smallest.

See also: Alloy; Ammunition; Armor, Bazooka; Bullet; Chemical and biological warfare; Explosive; Gun; Missile; Recoilless gun; Tank.

Arresting mechanism

When an aircraft lands on an aircraft carrier deck, its speed has to be cut from perhaps 150 mph (240 km/h) to rest in about 200 ft (60 m). The aircraft may well weigh up to 50,000 lb (23 tons), so the kinetic energy – the energy of motion – to be dissipated is considerable.

At the same time the retardation must be smooth: there must be no sudden snatch which might break the pilot's neck, overstress the aircraft's frame or disturb its landing path. Ideally, the retardation should be progressive, starting from nothing, building up to a maximum, then remaining constant until the aircraft finally comes to a standstill.

Arresting mechanisms are designed to achieve this aim, and in principle they all operate in the same way. At its tail end, the aircraft is fitted with a hinged hook which hangs below the level of the wheels of the aircraft during the landing run. As the plane comes in over the deck, the hook engages with a steel arresting wire stretched across the deck and raised a few inches by bow-shaped steel springs to allow the hook underneath. The ends of the arresting wire are connected to the energy absorbing gear, which has been further developed over the last few years to handle the increasing weight of modern aircraft combined with higher speeds.

The absorbing system widely used on British and American craft is based on the ram effect of a piston pushing hydraulic fluid through a control or throttling valve. As the arresting wire is pulled out it runs through guiding pulley wheels – or, in naval terms, *sheaves* – which transfer the movement to the ram through a series of pulleys mounted on both the fixed cylinder and the moving ram housed below the carrier deck.

Movement of the main arresting wire by, say, a distance of 16 ft (5 m) moves the final pulley, which is coupled to the piston, by only 1 ft (30 cm). This reduction in movement keeps the size of the piston within bounds and gives a useful mechanical advantage.

The retarding force is actually the hydraulic pressure in the cylinder, which depends on the ram speed. As the aircraft and therefore the ram slows, this force would decrease. So that the retardation

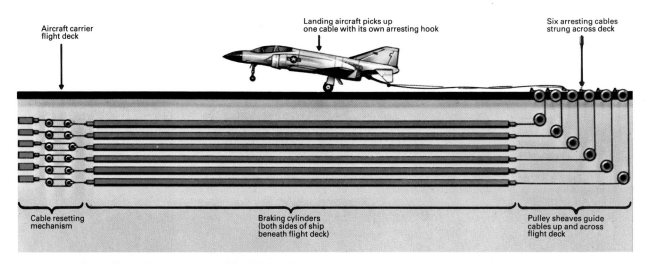

Aircraft carrier flight deck

Landing aircraft picks up one cable with its own arresting hook

Six arresting cables strung across deck

Cable resetting mechanism

Braking cylinders (both sides of ship beneath flight deck)

Pulley sheaves guide cables up and across flight deck

Above: In the water spray retarding system the landing aircraft catches one of the six cables stretched across the deck with its extended arrester hook. The need to decrease aircraft speeds on landing is not, however, confined to carriers. Under certain circumstances it is more convenient to use land-based arresting mechanisms for high speed aircraft rather than parachute brakes. Comparatively short landing strips were suitably equipped to take U.S. Navy fighter bombers during the Vietnamese campaign as did the British at Port Stanley airfield during the Falklands campaign. Left: An A-4 Skyhawk landing on the deck of the U.S.S. carrier Oriskany into a nylon barrier thrown up in order to stabilize the plane and pilot who had been injured.

remains constant, the control valve is arranged to provide greater restriction as more wire is pulled out. This can be adjusted to allow for different weights of aircraft.

The outflow from the hydraulic cylinder goes into a chamber, where it compresses a gas to store the energy. This energy is used to reset the system and pull the arresting wire back to its original position, the compressed gas forcing the hydraulic fluid back into the cylinder with the aid of a pump to overcome the energy losses in the system.

Resetting at speed is important when a large number of aircraft have to be landed in a short time. After an aircraft has landed, the arresting wire is inspected quickly for faults and then is pulled back tight across the deck, the whole operation taking only about 20 seconds.

The high weights of modern naval aircraft have made this arrangement unsuitable where deck space is limited. American vessels are larger than British built craft, and they have extended the flight deck to take the longer stopping space required. But in 1968, Britain's Ark Royal aircraft carrier was converted to a different system. The arresting wire remains but, instead of a hydraulic ram, a low-energy water spray system is used.

By contrast to the older system of pulleys, the new water spray is direct acting. A sheave takes the wire

Above: The Nimitz class aircraft carriers provide the U.S. Navy with conventional firepower that is unmatched by any other navy.

below decks as before but this time there is no mechanical reduction and the wire acts directly on a piston in a water filled cylinder 200 ft (60 m) long. Along this cylinder is a series of holes which are closed off progressively as the arresting wire is extended, giving a nearly constant force. Water sprays out of the holes but is caught by an outer cylinder around the main one.

An advantage of this system is that it can be programmed to handle a whole range of aircraft weighing from 10,000 to 50,000 lb (4.5 to 23 tons). It has, however, created a number of design problems – now overcome. Resetting time must still be as quick as the earlier system and this means moving the piston back over its entire length in perhaps 20 seconds, while making sure that the cylinder is completely full of water: any air pockets could give disastrous shocks to the aircraft being slowed down. One method of resetting uses a return arrangement based on a hydraulic cylinder called a jigger and a multisheave pulley system.

See also: Aircraft; Airplane; Energy; Hydraulic mechanism; Lever; Pressure; Pump.

Artificial intelligence

Artificial intelligence (AI) – the ability of a computer to think rather then simply process information – is possible to a limited extent with some of today's machines. The next step toward true artificial intelligence will come in the 1990s, with the advent of the Fifth generation of computers.

Marvin Minsky, an American pioneer of artificial intelligence, defined it as "the science of making machines do things that would require intelligence if done by men." A weakness of his definition, however, is that there is uncertainty about a clear definition for natural intelligence. As it stands, Minsky's definition of AI would include almost everything that computers do. For example, some of the earliest computers were engaged in working out complicated financial calculations for banks and insurance companies. Certainly, these tasks would require intelligence if done by people, but computerized tasks of this sort are not usually thought of as examples of AI.

Many of the tasks that come within the category of AI are already done by some of today's computers. They can solve problems, make decisions in difficult circumstances, learn, recognize complicated patterns (such as a signature or a face), prove theorems in geometry and logic, write their own programs and play games such as chess, checkers and backgammon with great skill. They can understand natural languages (such as English, French and Japanese) and teach ROBOTS how to take instructions. Sometimes a particular type of activity, such as learning or problem solving, is particularly important to many specific computerized tasks. For example, problem solving is equally important to a robot trying to find its way out of a maze and to a computer solving an end game in chess.

Computers are using AI when they show some initiative, when they work things out on their own (sometimes in ways that the human programer did not anticipate), and when they work in ways that seem to imitate some of the more impressive human mental activities (such as drawing logical conclusions or translating languages).

One man who considered the prospects not only of a thinking machine, but of a machine with superhuman intelligence, was British mathematician Alan Turing. In 1936, he proved mathematically that a machine could be taught, then went on to lead the team that built the first electronic computer, which was used by the British forces to decipher German codes during World War II. During this period, Turing also devised the definitive test – the Turing Test – long before others accepted the possibility of AI.

The participants in the Turing Test are two intelligent people and a thoroughly programed computer. The people converse via the computer, using keyboards and cathode ray terminals, and if the computer can subsitute for either of them and sustain the conversation without the other knowing, then it is at least as intelligent as they are. Four generations of computer have not achieved such a level of sophistication.

The first four generations of computers were based on electronics. Not included in these are many mechanical computing systems that have been developed over the centuries – long before the advent of electronics. Such mechanical systems – using levers, gears and connecting rods – were built

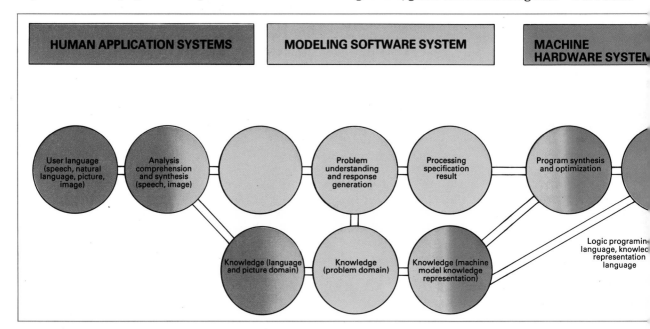

Above and right: Although not truly intelligent, today's systems are invaluable aids.

by Pascal and von Leibniz in the seventeenth century, Jacobson in the eighteenth and Babbage in the nineteenth century.

First generation computers (dating to the middle and later 1940s) were based on discharge tubes or VACUUM TUBES. The tubes tended to be unreliable and the computers were large and cumbersome (a typical first generation computer weighed 30 tons). Second generation computers used TRANSISTORS instead of tubes, following the pioneering work at the U.S. Bell Telephone Laboratories in the late 1940s. Transistors could do all the tasks done

by vacuum tubes, but were much smaller, more reliable, and required much less electrical energy to make them work.

Third generation computers employed INTEGRATED CIRCUITS, thin wafers of silicon containing circuit elements such as transistors, DIODES, RESISTORS and CAPACITORS. By this time, the individual electronic components were mere specks of chemicals on tiny pieces of silicon: it became possible to build thousands of components into electronic circuits which are the size of a fingernail.

Fourth generation computers (including today's industrial MICROPROCESSORS and personal computers) developed further the integration of large numbers of electronic components into tiny manufactured units: it became reasonable to imagine – through Very Large Scale Integration (VLSI) – building no fewer than a million electronic components into a silicon-based circuit about 0.16 square inch (1 cm square).

Development of the next generation of computers – the fifth – is well advanced. The Japanese plan to have a prototype built by 1991. These machines will continue the development of ever higher levels of integration (there have been references to Very-VLSI circuits), and they will introduce a range of new features. For example, it is likely that use will be made of substances other than silicon (though silicon will continue to be employed). New equipment designs will be introduced, and new computer languages developed – all expected to yield computers capable of handling knowledge and exercising intelligence. Fifth generation computers are intended to become more humanlike, able to under-

Symbol manipulation machine

Problem solving and inference machine

Numerical computer machine

Knowledge base machine

Database machine

Left: Fifth generation computers will have three basic systems – user interaction and input, software modeling and the processing and support hardware. Some progress has been made with the first two of these – for example, experiments with voice and pattern recognition machines, and programs. A robot arm linked to the computer can identify an object by comparing its image with one stored in its memory. Other machines can read handwriting.

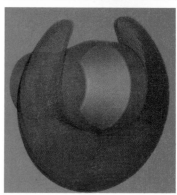

Above: The multi-million dollar 4 ton Cray-1 is one of the most powerful supercomputers available.

Above: This simulation of the airflow over the rear of a rocket traveling just below the speed of sound required over 10 billion arithmetical operations and took Cray-1 just 18 hours, representing a large saving in time, money and effort over wind tunnel tests.

stand human language and to hold conversations with their human users. There are already computers that can do this to a limited extent, but the computers of the 1990s will be much more sophisticated and knowledgeable.

Fifth generation hardware

Computer *hardware*, the physical equipment out of which the machines are built, can be considered as having two main aspects. The first is the range of substances out of which the electronic components can be made; the second is the way in which the components are assembled – the "architecture" of the computer. Most electronic computers have been based on silicon, which, as an electrical semiconductor, has properties that are well suited to today's computer circuits. Much research is focusing on various other substances that could prove useful in the computers of the future. A leading substance of this sort is gallium arsenide (GaAs), which can operate either at room temperature or at artificially maintained low temperatures, where electronic pulses can move at unusually high speeds. Integrated GaAs circuits have already been developed, and first indications are that fifth gener-

ation circuits might be variously built up out of silicon, gallium arsenide, indium phosphate and other substances.

New architectures will also be a main feature of fifth generation machines. Most electronic computers have relied upon a sequential processing of information, by which one task is completed before another is started. To achieve the expected levels of intelligence, tomorrow's machines should be able to process vast amounts of information rapidly. The fastest rates are achieved only if many tasks can be worked on at the same time. This sort of arrangement is called *parallel processing*. It follows that, whereas today's computers usually have one central processing unit (CPU), fifth generation computers will probably have thousands, each working on separate stages of a task. Such computers could rely on sequential processing for simple tasks, but exploit parallel processing when high speed performance (for example, obeying hundreds of millions of instructions every second) is required.

Fifth generation software

Computer hardware is of no use unless it is linked with software – various sequences of instructions, or *programs*, that computers follow to do particular tasks. However sophisticated the hardware, the skill of the human programer is crucial in exploiting the computer to best advantage, and the wider the range of software, the more versatile will be the computer. An important facility is the computer language in which programs are written. Just as some human languages are better suited than others to particular purposes, the same is true of computer languages. For example, Russian is said to be a rich language for poetry, whereas English is more suitable for expression in science and technology. Similarly, some computer languages are suitable for financial calculations, others for scientific research and yet others for the control of robots. Evidently, tomorrow's computers will need programs written in languages that are suitable for the intelligent knowledge-handling tasks that these machines will be expected to perform.

Various existing computer languages are expected to influence the development of languages for fifth generation computers. For example, the language PROLOG (short for PROgraming in LOGic) has been developed to assist the reasoning powers of computers. It has been adopted as a *kernel language* by the designers of software for fifth generation computers. Computer languages, like human languages, evolve in use, generating dialects and new languages. For instance, POPLOG – a mixture of PROLOG and LISP (another AI language) – is being used in AI research and might be useful for fifth generation software. Using developments of these and other languages, such as DURAL, VALID and occam, there is likely to be less burden on human programers.

Applications

Computers will gradually learn to write most of their own programs and, moreover, to understand human languages. Using an extensive knowledge base, they will be able to solve problems, discussing the difficulties with human users. Already, there are *expert systems* working in disciplines such as medical diagnosis, geological prospecting, chemical analysis, chemical synthesis, mathematics, engineering design, and education. A central feature of expert systems is that they can manipulate (think about) a large store of knowledge – compiled from the memory of the world's experts in each discipline. They can also carry on a dialog with human beings – most working expert systems have some sort of conversational ability. Fifth generation computers are expected to develop such advisory and conversational skills, rendering such machines more able to understand human problems in tackling particular tasks. The MYCIN medical diagnostic system has already proven a better disease diagnostician than human physicians in some contexts; the Prospector geological system has

Below left: Conventional computers tackle problems one step at a time through serial processing (A) whereas supercomputers break a problem up and begin tackling it from all sides at once through the system of parallel processing (B). Below: An auto-imaging machine is capable of seeing objects.

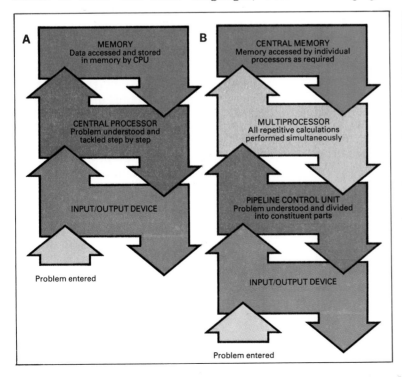

A
MEMORY
Data accessed and stored in memory by CPU

CENTRAL PROCESSOR
Problem understood and tackled step by step

INPUT/OUTPUT DEVICE

Problem entered

B
CENTRAL MEMORY
Memory accessed by individual processors as required

MULTIPROCESSOR
All repetitive calculations performed simultaneously

PIPELINE CONTROL UNIT
Problem understood and divided into constituent parts

INPUT/OUTPUT DEVICE

Problem entered

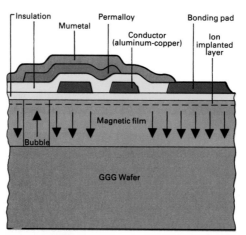

Left: A cross-section of a bubble memory – one of the devices being developed that could have applications in tomorrow's intelligent computers. The memory is formed from a single crystal of garnet grown on a wafer in an accurately controlled furnace. The circuits are traced (below left) on the crystal, which is then etched, cut into chips, and packaged (far left) in highly sterile, dust-free conditions.

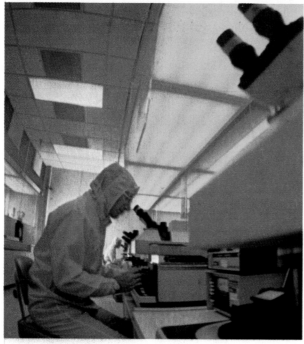

outperformed human beings in at least one celebrated case; MACSYMA has a wider range of mathematical skills than most mathematicians. Fifth generation *experts* will be more skilled than any of today's systems. Already, much faster, more powerful and more *friendly* systems are becoming available for use on today's microcomputers.

Such developments can be regarded as an inevitable boon – people will be assisted in every imaginable sphere by highly intelligent machines. Viewed pessimistically, however, they may amount to a dangerous transfer of expertise from human beings to computers, with too many important decisions, for example on health, warmaking and politics, being left to computer judgment. Either interpretation can be argued, but human beings are still in a position to choose how tomorrow's computers will affect tomorrow's society and to what extent.

• FACT FILE •

- In the early 1900s a Spanish inventor constructed a machine that could play chess and checkmate its opponent with a rook and a king versus a king. Later chess computer programs, developed in the 1950s, could not play nearly as well as the people who wrote them. But in 1977 a chess computer program won the Minnesota Open Tournament, performing well up to master level.

- Using very-large-scale-integration (VLSI) semiconductor chips capable of high capacities and speeds, Japanese scientists are working on a national computer project to produce a super-intelligent *fifth generation* computer ready for commercial use by the early 1990s. Among other functions, the computer will be able to listen to instructions, help to program itself, translate many foreign languages, make logical inferences and learn from its own experiences and mistakes.

- A commercially produced domestic robot being taken around the country to be demonstrated to dealers was programed by its demonstrator to respond to airport security checks. When the security staff opened its carton, the robot perceived the light by means of a photo-cell eye, and exclaimed, via its voice synthesizer, "It sure feels good to get out of that *bleep-bleep* box."

See also: Binary; Computer, Computer graphics; Data storage; Microchip.

Artificial joint and limb

The great increase in interdisciplinary cooperation between medical science and modern, high-technology engineering techniques has expedited the use of manufactured replacements for bones and joints and given a boost to artificial limb technology.

The study of these devices is known as *prosthetics*; bones and joints are called *endoprostheses*, because they are implanted within the body, whereas artificial limbs are *external prostheses*.

The latest figures show that in the U.S. in 1983, about 45,000 amputations were conducted and that the total amputee population was some 400,000 patients. The ratio of males to females was 2 to 1, and for every arm amputated, 16 legs were involved. Hip joint replacement is by far the most common of the implant operations. In the lower extremity, the knee is a much less common operation and the ankle is only rarely performed on an experimental basis.

In the upper extremity, finger joint replacement is almost entirely performed to relieve pain and severe deformity, due to arthritic conditions, followed to a lesser extent by the elbow and shoulder joints. Increasingly, massive long bone reconstructive surgery is decreasing the need for high-level amputations, particularly for tumor patients where the disease originates in the bone and has not been transmitted to the soft tissues.

Endoprostheses

These are required where bone and joint tissues are beyond repair. The hard, crystalline nature of bone gives it an inert appearance. It is, however, a living tissue which provides a calcium and phosphate store for the body, and produces bone marrow, a blood-forming tissue. Bone is made up of *osteocytes*, which are crystalline minerals interlayered with fibrous protein. These are constantly changing and the cells involved in the regenerative process are *osteoblasts*, which lay down new bone and *osteoclasts*, which absorb dead tissue.

Bone is PIEZOELECTRIC, which means that its electrical characteristics change as a function of the forces applied to it. Trabecular growth in bone also is directed along the lines of principal stresses imposed upon them. This can give rise to problems with amputated limbs developing *Spur* growth in areas of pressure. By inducing similar minute electrical potentials in the bone, the regenerative pro-

Below: Researchers study the gait of a non-handicapped person, photographed with marker dots, to help them design artificial legs.

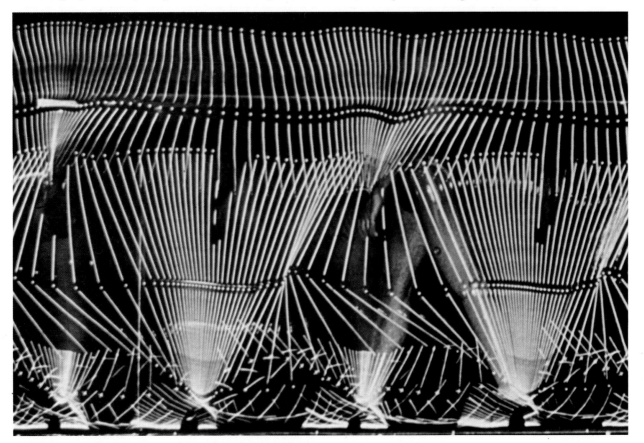

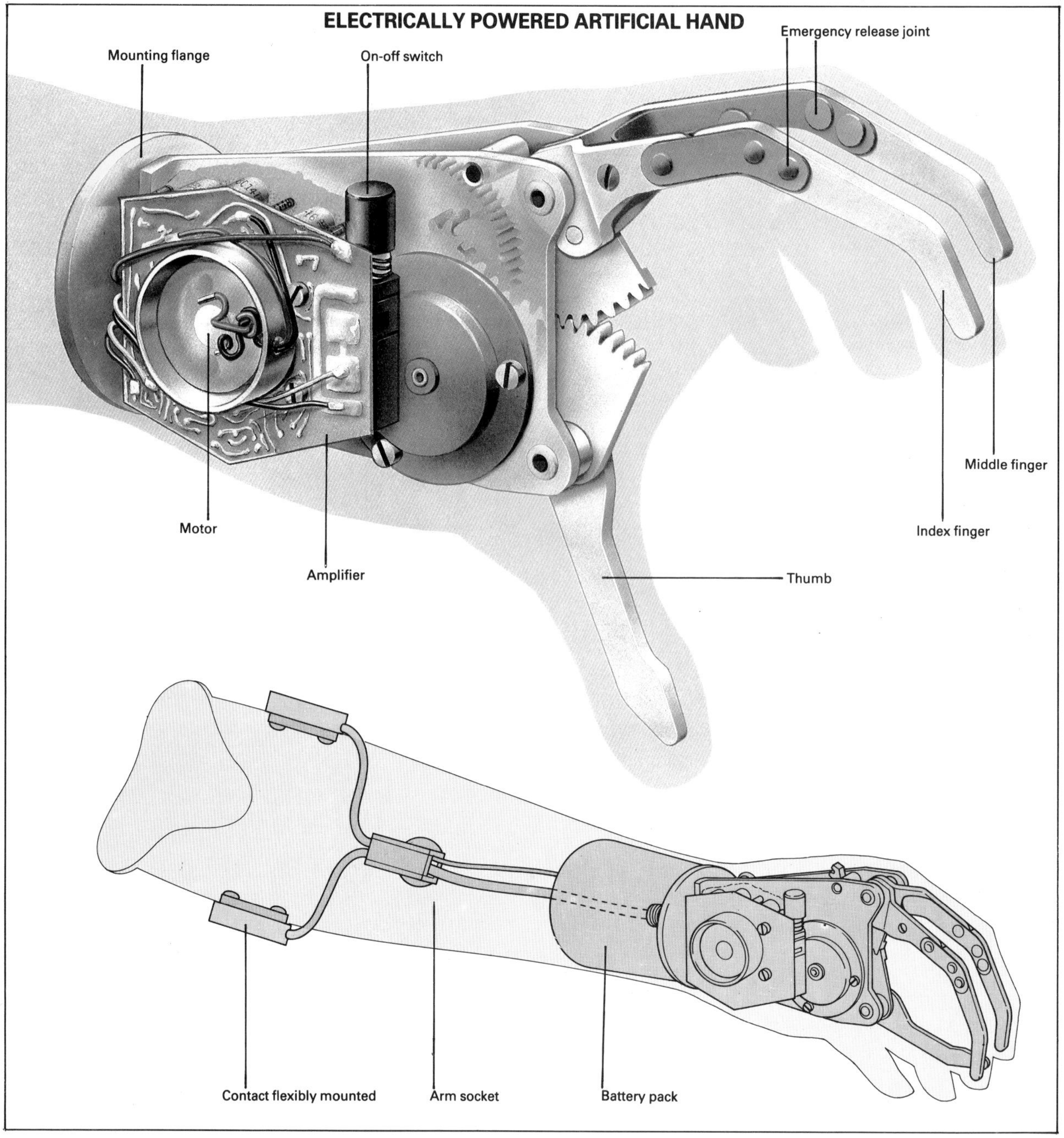

ELECTRICALLY POWERED ARTIFICIAL HAND

Mounting flange

On-off switch

Emergency release joint

Motor

Amplifier

Middle finger

Index finger

Thumb

Contact flexibly mounted

Arm socket

Battery pack

Above: The electrically powered Viennatone Myomot MM4 artificial hand is a simple design which is easy to use, as well as being a fine tool.

cess can be increased. These modern techniques often result in speedier recovery. The tiny currents are induced by electromagnets, and the procedure is termed *electromagnetic bone stimulation*.

Bone tissue, however, surprisingly is more easily destroyed by high pressure than soft tissues. This must be carefully considered in the design of the fixing of the implant with the surrounding bone

tissue and is one of the physician's greatest concerns.

Osteocytes are nourished by *plasma* derived from the blood. This contains neither the red (erythrocytes) nor the white (leucocytes) corpuscles. The protective mechanisms of the blood, which attack foreign and infectious bodies in the system, are not present, so artificial replacements are not rejected by the body. However, where such replacements do come into contact with the blood and soft tissue, particularly from wear debris of articulating prostheses, care must be taken so as not to initiate any immune response. About 8 per cent of implant

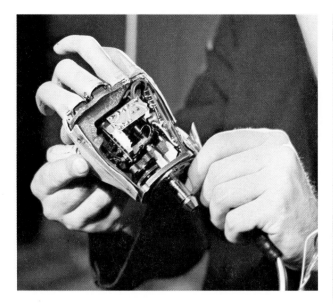

Above: Power for this motorized hand is supplied from a battery pack mounted at the wrist. Sensors pick up the electrical inpulses from the wearer's remaining nerves and amplify them to drive the fingers. With practice, the user can operate the hand just by willing it to move. Right: A machine tests the endurance of an artificial foot.

patients have an allergic reaction in this way and it may often be necessary to remove the implant.

Joints

There are many types of joints in the body, each adapted to the particular function, degree of movement, and control required. Usually, the two bone surfaces forming the articulation are covered with a layer of *cartilage*, a tough yet pliable matrix of fibers with a glassy, smooth surface. Sometimes there is a further layer called the *fibrocartilage* or *meniscus*. The bones are tied together with very tough bands or capsules of fibrous tissues called *ligaments*, and the whole joint is partially lined by the *synovial membrane*. This membrane secretes a transparent, yellowish-white or reddish fluid called *synovia*. If either the synovial fluid is not produced or it crystallizes, or the articular cartilage loses its smooth properties, the joint becomes stiff and painful and can even seize up completely. This can result in the replacement of the whole or part of the joint.

The particular problems here are to find very hard-wearing materials which have low coefficient of sliding friction. The latest research techniques indicate that a microthin layer of nitrogen atoms may extend the life of such joints. This ion implantation process yields a device which is extremely resistant to mechanical wear and body fluid corrosion and minimizes the release of metal particles into the surrounding tissue.

Choice of materials

Metal alloys are used to reduce the problems of corrosion and fatigue that render pure metals useless as bone substitutes. They can never, however, eliminate them completely.

Vitallium is one such alloy, consisting of 65 per cent cobalt, 30 per cent chromium and 3 per cent molybdenum with traces of manganese, silicon and carbon. Unfortunately, this material is so hard that it cannot be machined and has to be cast to the exact shape required. Careful monitoring of the manufacturing process is, therefore, necessary, including X ray examination and crack detection techniques, so that the slightest flaw is detected. A stainless steel alloy with 18 per cent chromium and 12 per cent nickel can be machined, although there are some problems with corrosion and tissue reaction.

Titanium is increasingly used for joints as well as bone plates and screws. It is unique among structural metals in that 99.8 per cent pure metal (commercially pure) can have varying degrees of strength and ductility by altering the amount of oxygen and nitrogen gas dissolved in solid solution. The proportion varies from 0.04 per cent to 0.08 per cent. Titanium, however, must not be used in contact with itself because it welds cold.

Implants, particularly femoral head implant prostheses, can be cemented into the femur using cold-setting acrylic cement, commonly used as dental cement. Such cement is slightly exothermic

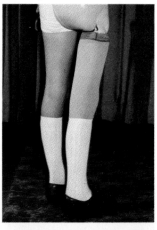

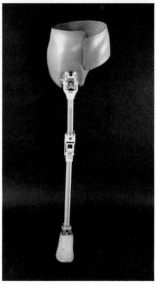

Above: A Myomot MM4 electrically-powered hand gives the user good grasp, but manipulating small objects is more difficult. An artificial leg (above right) does not appear readily obvious once the user is fully dressed, and although its mechanism (right below) is simpler than the hand, its design is just as challenging.

in setting, which means that heat is generated as it cures. This heat does not destroy too many bone cells and the hardened cement distributes the stresses fairly evenly to the surrounding bone, which can then regenerate itself unhindered.

Recent research indicates that the stem of bone implants can be finely coated with the ceramic materials into which calcified bone will grow, so there is no need to cement the joints.

External prostheses
Artificial limbs can be broadly categorized into two groups: upper and lower extremities (arms and legs). The problems encountered by the prosthetic

designer for each of these levels are quite different. In the upper extremity the major problems are associated with manipulation and control of many joints, whereas in the lower extremity the problems are of a structural engineering nature, requiring components of very high strength which are not prohibitive in weight.

Amputation is a mutilating operation, but in many cases of trauma and disease it is necessary as a life-saving procedure, or in order to improve the quality of life. Nearly all amputees experience the sensation of feeling the missing limb – this is a normal phenomenon called *Phantom limb*. These sensations eventually subside, but may take many months or even years. Prosthetic use usually reduces these sensations. *Phantom pain*, however, can occur after amputation of patients who have had a history of pain in the limb prior to surgery. It does not occur in disarticulations. Modern treatments, such as *transcutaneous electrical nerve stimulation* (TENS) can often provide relief where such pain hinders recovery.

Above: Leg manufacture reached near production line pace at this World War I limb-fitting center in Britain. They were made mostly of wood.

Artificial legs

Artificial legs fitted today are passive devices; the power supply needed to move them would, in any case, be prohibitively large and they are required to function in several quite different modes.

Firstly, they must support the total weight of the whole body rapidly applied at heel contact. Secondly, the joints must be secured so that the limb segments move in a natural fashion with little or no perceivable limp. Finally, the replacements must have a normal, external shape, feel and appearance so that the patient develops phillic rather than phobic attitudes towards it, and thus allows the amputee to walk comfortably with confidence and, above all, safely.

To achieve this, perhaps the most important feature of the prostheses is the socket. This is the person-machine interface through which all the body forces are transmitted. Great care is taken to ensure that an accurate replica of the remaining stump is taken and, after appropriate modification, is used to manufacture the socket.

Air pressure casting is one of the modern techniques routinely used today to achieve such an accurate impression of the stump. The latest international research uses laser HOLOGRAPHY to scan the stump and build a three-dimensional computer model, the surface of which may then be topologically modified for weight bearing. This computer-generated shape is then manufactured in hard wax to produce the socket, which must be carefully and individually fitted to the stump. Areas

which are sensitive or tender must be skillfully relieved of pressure.

The simplest replacements for the foot consist of polyurethane molded components which are light, robust and are manufactured in standard shoe sizes. The inherent flexibility of the material is carefully controlled so that the required toe joint movements and stiffness are simulated.

The ankle joint often has two bearing assemblies, mutually perpendicular, to provide planta and dorsiflexion (up and down movement) of the foot as well as inversion and eversion (side-to-side movements). Aircraft type bearings, which are sealed and lubricated for life, are used and devices to adjust heel height are also incorporated. At the heel and instep, natural rubber springs are fitted, the stiffness of which are adjusted to suit the individual requirements of the patient and which absorb impact at heel strike, allow a smooth roll-over during mid-stance and release stored elastic energy during the *push-off* phase for forward propulsion during the final period of stance.

Modern modular limb systems often incorporate a rotational device to absorb torsional energy. This is particularly helpful to the younger, active patient and helps, for example, a golfer to swing.

The knee joint firstly must prevent the leg from buckling or collapsing when full body weight is applied to it. Secondly, the mechanisms must provide control of pendulation in the free-swinging phase when weight is on the contralateral leg; this function is called *cadence control*. Thirdly, the knee must provide a cushioned stop to absorb terminal impact at the end of the swing phase and to prevent hyperextension. Finally, it must feed back to the patient at all times the exact position and condition of the limb *(proprioception)*.

Knee stability can simply be achieved by carefully positioning the knee joint in relation to the load line through the limb. This is referred to as *alignment stability*. Alternatively, a friction brake-type device can be used. Polycentric mechanisms and linkages are often used, as are hydraulic systems. Swing-phase controls can be either simple friction or pneumatic, or hydraulic, dampers. The latter permit the amputee to walk at different speeds (they are *velocity sensitive*) without the need to readjust the mechanism.

The latest modular hip joints incorporate an alignment device such that the joint can be positioned on the anterior/distal (frontal end), aspects of the pelvic socket. This enables the amputee to adopt a very natural sitting position and helps with the stability of this very high-level artificial leg. Most prostheses for this level also incorporate a stride adjustment to control the angle of hip flexion movement. For the patient to sit down, this control must be overridden. When the patient stands up, however, the mechanism will automatically reset itself to the walk mode.

The latest modular limbs have soft cosmetic restoration, so that they feel and look most natural. The whole of the leg has a soft polyurethane cover, individually shaped to match that of the other leg. Finally, a skin-colored, nylon reinforced silicon sleeve covers the whole of the leg and all the joints. This results in a pleasing appearance which is waterproof and hygienic.

Artificial arms

Artificial hands and arms are used in many different situations, depending on the level of amputation – the higher the level of amputation, the greater the functional loss and, therefore, the problems of rehabilitation become much bigger.

Artificial arms can be generally categorized into two types: body-powered and externally powered. Body-powered limbs are so called because they rely on body movement elsewhere for their function and control. The hand, for example, is an extremely intricate and versatile instrument and presents a tremendous challenge to the designer. Not only must the replacement be functional, but its cosmetic appearance must also be pleasing – not just to the patient, but also to others. For example, it is imperative that the prosthetic hand of a little child be pleasing to the mother.

A simple spring mechanism can enable the patient to grasp and hold an object; this is the most fundamental use of the hand and is termed *prehension*. The force provided by this simple spring, however, cannot be easily used for both heavy grips and delicate, precision objects.

The other, more practical, approach is the simple

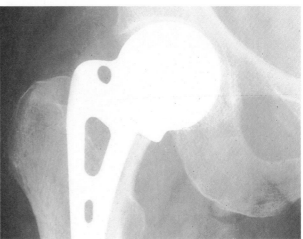

Top: Artificial hip joints cast by the lost wax process from an alloy that is too tough to be machined. The castings are cleaned then X rayed (above) to make sure they are free from defects.

hand-substitute – the split hook. This is light, cheap and surprisingly functional for an experienced user. Many different attachments for varying requirements can be speedily interchanged. The big disadvantage, however, is that it is rather ugly.

Where the arm has to be replaced, correct length, weight and comfort are very important factors for a well-balanced replacement. Much use is made of composite materials such as fiber-reinforced polyester resin which combines strength and stiffness with lightness and ease of shaping. Movement and control are provided by the remaining muscles in the stump, or from the shoulder, transmitted through a simple harness system and operated by cables.

For amputations above the elbow, the prosthetic elbow unit is one of the most important components. It must permit bending of the forearm and provide locking of the joint at will.

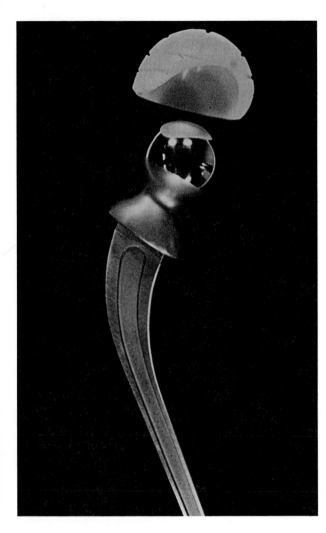

Above: A complete hip joint made from stainless steel. The socket, into which the ball fits in the pelvis, is made of polyethylene. Friction is minimized by giving the ball a high polish.

Where the shoulder has to be amputated (this is called a *forequarter amputation*), a body harness is used. A device has been developed in which the patient operates the elbow lock, using the chin; the forearm and hand are then moved by shrugging the contralateral shoulder which has a harness and connecting cables attached.

Externally powered limbs

The comparatively recent development of advanced and miniaturized SERVOMECHANISMS has made it possible to design externally powered limbs. Most of the research and development took place as a result of the Thalidomide disaster. Thalidomide is a drug which was found to produce gross abnormalities in the children of women who took it during pregnancy. The problems were far more acute than those of the normal surgical amputee, because the casual-ties often had no limbs at all, or were very severely deformed, sometimes at both extremities.

Of the various attempts which were made to help these cases, the most successful were pneumatically powered fluidic devices. These limbs had small cylinders of compressed carbon dioxide gas, connected by rubber tubing through a system of valves to pistons mounted in the interior of the arm. This enabled movements about the shoulder, elbow and wrist joints as well as prehension of the hand.

The latest powered arms use miniature, permanent-magnet DC motors, supplied by small rechargeable 6V battery packs. These may be operated either by microswitches attached to adjacent muscles or MYOELECTRICALLY by sensing the nerve signals from the antagonistic muscle groups remaining in the stump. Ranges of hands and elbows are now routinely fitted to children and adults. The electronic control systems use CMOS logic and integrated circuits to control, for example, the prehension force and gripping and opening speed of the hand.

Probably the most sophisticated hand in the world is being developed at the University of Southampton in Britain. This robotic hand is fully articulated with an intelligent control system.

The Southampton design significantly reduces the amount of conscious effort the patient requires to operate the mechanism. The computer-controlled system is a hierarchy at the top of which is a logic decision processor. This can identify any one of six basic high-level command states – touch, hold, squeeze, maneuver, release, and relax – from a single patient input. Touch-sensitive devices in the fingers and the palm of the hand, directional slipsensors in the thumb, as well as force and position-sensing transducers in the fingers and thumb, feed all the necessary information to the decision processor.

The patient thus gives an overall command to grip an object and the sensors, via the intelligent controller, actuate the hand mechanism to perform the most effective grip configuration according to the shape, weight, and compliance of the object being gripped. The fingers are articulated at the relevant joints and flexed by artificial tendons – nylon webbing wound up by servomotor spools. The entire hand is powered by four miniature sumarium cobalt permanent magnet DC motors. This hand, however, although having great potential for the patient, is still only a research tool.

The major problem with this and other sophisticated hands is the design of a cosmetic glove which will not impair the function of the hand.

See also: Alloy; Bone structure; Electric motor; Fracture treatment; Holography; Immunology; Servomechanism; Transplant surgery.

Asbestos

The use of blue asbestos has been banned in many countries because of its danger to health. Other types of asbestos remain in use, but will be gradually replaced by alternative materials when they become available.

Asbestos is widely used as a heat insulating, fireproof material. It is fibrous in nature, which tends to disguise the fact that it is a mineral found in rock seams, and obtained by mining. There are various types of asbestos, but they are all basically silicates of metals such as magnesium, calcium or sodium.

For most of its long history asbestos has been used for making clothing, its fire resistance being regarded as a mysterious but fortunate property without being particularly well exploited. In ancient times, asbestos was used as wick material for lamps, which accounts for its rather paradoxical derivation from the Greek word *asbeston*, which means unquenchable or inextinguishable.

There are two main types of asbestos. *Chrysotile* or *white* asbestos is the more widely used and historically longer known variety. Its richest sources are in Canada (Quebec) and in the Ural Mountains of the U.S.S.R. The other is a group known as *amphibole* asbestos, whose chief members are *crocidolite* (typically blue in color) and *amosite* (typically ash gray or fawn), both extensively mined in southern Africa. Chrysotile fibers tend to be shorter and softer than amphiboles and have a

higher melting point (and so a greater fire resistance), which means that they are particularly suitable for weaving into fireproof fabrics. The amphiboles, having high tensile strength, are useful as reinforcement fibers in the production of composite materials such as asbestos cement and certain fiber reinforced plastics.

Because research in the early 1960s revealed the health hazards associated with crocidolite (blue) asbestos, it has not been imported or used in many

Above right: Workers clearing asbestos wall and ceiling sidings and linings wear special clothing and breathing apparatus to protect them from the dust. Right: Racing drivers currently protect themselves from the inherent risk of fire with suits made from Du Pont's Nomex – a nylon-type fabric – rather than asbestos. Far right: In the case of protection for firefighters who are required to work in very high temperature conditions, there is still little substitute for flameproof suits made of asbestos. It is still the cheapest and most durable material.

countries since then and the use of amosite fiber is to a very large extent today obsolete.

Mining asbestos

Chrysotile fibers occur as seams in the soft rock serpentine, which is found close to the Earth's surface. The asbestos ore is obtained by quarrying or by *block caving*. In the latter technique a mass of rock is undermined so that it falls and breaks into pieces under its own weight while passing down a chute into haulage trucks below. Amphiboles, on the other hand, occur in rich but narrow seams lying at virtually any incline from horizontal to vertical, necessitating mines that may run as deep as 1000 ft (300 m) or more beneath the surface.

Only about 10 per cent of the ore is actual asbestos. In some cases, good long veins can be removed by hand, but usually the fibers have to be removed mechanically. A series of crushers deals with lumps of different sizes, the fibers being sucked out.

Uses of asbestos

Products consisting solely or chiefly of asbestos are invariably made from asbestos yarn. This is produced by weaving or plaiting the longer and better quality fibers just as if they were wool or cotton. Typical products include insulating tapes, cloth, brake linings, gaskets, packings, rope and gas filters. Fireproof gloves and clothing and theater safety curtains are also made in this way. In these applications the material may sometimes be wire reinforced, or impregnated with substances such as rubber, graphite and resins.

The shorter fibers, *shingles*, are used in the production of composite materials, of which the oldest and best known is asbestos cement. This was invented in the late nineteenth century by the owner of a Viennese paper and board making plant. He found that millboard treated with a mixture of about 20 per cent asbestos fiber and 80 per cent cement produced a new material with many possible applications. The paper maker began to market asbestos cement in flat sheets 15 in. (40 cm) square and this more than anything created a market for asbestos.

Manufacture

The first stage in the manufacture of asbestos cement is to produce a *slurry* by mixing cement and asbestos fibers in water. A coating of slurry is then applied to a moving belt and the water drained off. The thin coating is transferred to a rotating cylinder where further layers are built up. When the coating is thick enough, the damp, flexible sheet can be removed and molded into the required shape. It is allowed to dry and mature for three weeks. Asbestos cement sheeting is fire resistant and weatherproof and remains one of the most widely

Above: Crocidolite or "blue" asbestos is no longer used because of its serious health risks.

used building materials, especially for the exterior siding of industrial and agricultural buildings. Other useful properties such as thermal and acoustic insulation can be improved by variations in composition, producing insulating sheet and tiles for internal wall and ceiling linings.

Pressure pipes are another important use for asbestos cement, and followed quickly from the original development of the materials. Today they are commonly produced by feeding a thick asbestos slurry on to a revolving metal former or *mandrel*. The slurry sticks to the outside of the mandrel, which may be up to 16 ft (5 m) long, and is slid off the end and oven dried.

Asbestos fibers are also used either alone or in conjunction with GLASS FIBER for the production of reinforced plastics. Typical applications include corrosion resistant lining in pipelines, storage vessels for chemical industry equipment and shatterproof moldings for automobile components.

Health and safety

Despite its long history of use, especially on an increasing industrial scale since the mid nineteenth century, the potential health hazards associated with asbestos did not become seriously apparent until after World War II. The biggest problem in researching asbestos related diseases is the long time lag between the first exposure through inhaling high levels of asbestos dust, and the onset of one of the three principle diseases – asbestosis, lung cancer and mesothelioma (a tumor of the membrane which covers the lungs). The time lag can range between 20 and 50 years.

The rising incidence of lung disease (asbestosis) among workers who were working or had worked with asbestos from the early 1900s onwards led to increasingly tougher regulations to control its use.

See also: Cement; Firefighting; Flame and flashpoint; Flame retardant fabric; Glass, fiber.

Asdic and sonar

Asdic (called after the Allied Submarine Detection Investigation Committee) is a device developed originally for detecting submarines by means of sound waves travelling through water. Since World War II its usefulness has grown and now includes detectors for submerged wrecks and shoals of fish, navigational aids for ships, devices to measure the depth of water under a ship and equipment for oceanographic research purposes.

Sonar stands for sound navigation ranging and this has replaced the name asdic. Another term, *echo sounding*, implies the principle of the system. Sound is normally thought of as being wavelike vibrations of the air, but water can also transmit vibrations. By analyzing water-borne echoes electronically a picture of the area below the surface can be obtained.

In the basic technique, a short pulse of sound, which may be within the range audible to humans or may be on a much higher frequency, is transmitted from the bottom of the ship, usually by way of a TRANSDUCER mounted in a hole cut in the ship's bottom. (A transducer is any device that converts electrical power into another form, such as sound, or vice versa.) The sound pulse travels downward until it strikes the sea bottom or a submerged object, which reflects it back to the ship. There, it is picked up by another transducer, and the time taken for the pulse to travel down and back is measured. The speed at which sound travels in water depends on temperature, but it is approximately 4800 ft/s (1460 m/s), over four times its speed in air. The distance the pulse has travelled can be determined

Above: Modern scanning sonars can build up a detailed image of the sea bed using sonar-derived information processed by computer.

Left: The Hi-res VDU of a scanning sonar can easily distinguish between the sea bed, shoals of fish or, in this case, a submarine (below) observed from an acute angle.

from the measurement of the time it took to travel that distance.

Each pulse lasts anything from a few thousandths of a second to a few seconds depending upon the range of the particular sonar (the longer the range, the longer the pulse). The pulses are emitted at intervals ranging from a fraction of a second to a few seconds or even minutes, again depending upon range. A typical shipboard echo sounder used for navigation has two range scales. On its shorter range it will measure depths up to 20 ft (6 m) in steps of a fraction of a foot. On its longer range it will measure depths up to 100 or more fathoms (1 fathom = 6 ft = 1.8 m).

The time interval, and therefore the range, can be measured by a rotating disc carrying a neon tube which flashes when the reflected sound pulse (the echo) is picked up. The disc rotates at a constant speed, carrying the neon tube past a fixed circular

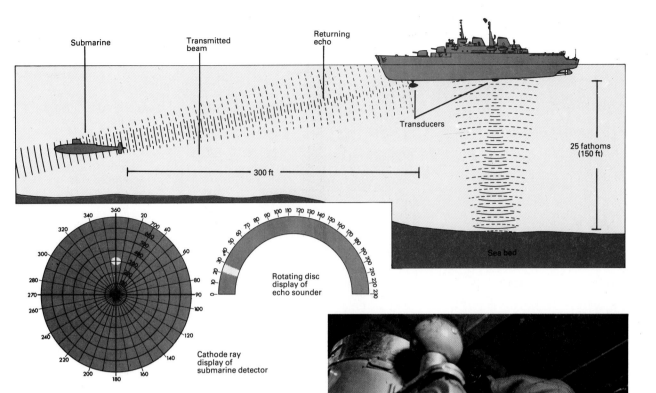

Above: A typical antisubmarine craft has two transducers. The signals from the fixed transducer are used to measure the depth – indicated on the rotating disk – and the forward array rotates through 360° to locate nearby submarines – indicated on the cathode ray tube. Right: An asdic operator on an Allied convoy escort ship in 1943.

scale graduated in terms of distance. The neon tube is at the top alongside the zero mark when the pulse is transmitted. If the echo sounder is set to a maximum range of 100 fathoms the neon tube will be carried full circle, that is, halfway round. The scale at this point is marked 50 fathoms, since the signal has travelled twice as far as the depth. In some units a permanent record is provided by a rotating stylus that darkens electrically sensitive paper when the echo is picked up. Other units have a CATHODE RAY TUBE display similar to a TV screen. In all cases the distance is read directly from a scale which may be calibrated in feet, fathoms or meters.

All merchant and naval vessels carry an echo sounder, the simplest form of sonar used only to measure the depth of water. Fishing vessels also carry a sonar that shows the depth and location of shoals of fish, but naval and research sonar is considerably more powerful and complex. The sound pulses are concentrated into narrow beams by mechanical horns in a manner similar to that in loud-speaking equipment.

Alternatively, the beams can be produced by placing a series of transducers in a line along the ship's bottom. Although each transducer sends out signals in all directions, the signals radiated from the different transducers interfere constructively and destructively with each other. In one particular direction the interference effects are constructive, the signals add together, and a powerful beam is transmitted in that direction. In all other directions the signals interfere destructively and cancel each other out so that very little energy is transmitted in other directions. The direction in which the beam points can be changed easily and quickly by altering the electrical timing of the signals fed to different transducers.

Sonar is essentially an intelligence gathering device and, as such, does not have to be moveable or attached to ship hulls to be useful. In modern naval warfare the capital ships are nuclear submarines and hostile boats are hunted by both strategic and tactical sonar arrays.

Left: Helicopters can move much faster than ships and it is possible to make rapid searches or surveys of submarine activity by lowering sonar into the sea from a hovering helicopter. This is a horizontal scanning sonar device from which an array of transducers are positioned appropriately to generate a flat, horizontal beam. The search area can be widened even further by shore-based for carrier-borne aircraft which can drop passive sonar or other sensors beyond helicopter range. Both systems have their limitations, though: passive sonars often having difficulty picking out a boat's signature from other undersea noises; and active sonar reflections can be distorted by changes in sea temperature, forming blind areas.

The U.S. Navy is probably the only service to have a considerable strategic sonar capability. For many years it has been seeding choke points in the oceans with passive, listening hydrophones (underwater microphones) which can record ships' engine noises so accurately that they can tell one class of ship from another. The latest SOSUS (Sound Surveillance System) guards the edge of the American continental shelf and the entrance to the Atlantic through the Greenland-Iceland-Britain gap. It is backed up by SURTASS (Surveillance Towed Array) systems in which standing patrols tow long arrays of passive sonar listening devices at slow speed over wide areas. Information from SOSUS and SURTASS is fed into the U.S. Navy's Antisubmarine Warfare Center's Command and Control computers which attempt to unscramble an overall picture of the numbers and general whereabouts of potentially hostile boats in the Atlantic.

DARPA (U.S. Defence Advanced Research Projects Agency) is experimenting with immensely long linear acoustic sonar arrays which transmit their findings by satellite to a central computer. These devices hear a tremendous clutter of under-sea noises from snapping shrimps to ship propellers and it is the computer's job to weed out the distant acoustics of a submarine's passage from all the other recorded sounds.

Sonar is also the backbone of tactical antisubmarine warfare in which naval forces try to protect themselves and their sea area from submarine attack. Active transducers can send out pulses in a much finer beam if there is a long array of them so a recently introduced technique is to tow a line of sonars behind a submarine hunting warship. There is not much speed loss and the finer beam means that hostile boats can be detected at longer range.

To increase a fleet's underwater reach helicopters can be deployed both to drop passive, listening sonar buoys and to dunk active transducers in the sea. The passive sonars will radio back information about ships engine noises or returning sound pulses to the helicopter or a command ship. The active sonar transducers dunked in the sea work just as those in ships' hulls.

See also: Cathode ray tube; Fishing industry; Ship; Submarine; Warship.

Assembly line

The assembly line provides the basis of modern mass production methods, enabling large quantities of a variety of goods to be produced at relatively low cost and consistent quality.

Its effectiveness relies on the fact that the manufacture of anything can be broken down into steps of great simplicity. An assembly line starts with the most basic component of the object to be manufactured and then adds each part in turn in a predetermined sequence until the final product emerges. Although a straight forward procedure in theory, the assembly line is a highly complex and detailed operation when considered step-by-step.

Manual lines

Early assembly lines, which provided the means to realize the full potential of the Industrial Revolution, were practically all run by manual labour. Most trivial tasks involved in the manufacture of even the most complicated objects were performed by hand. As each component was attached the evolving assembly was passed on to the next stage of the line by hand where it had a new part added before being passed on again.

Factory workers spent their whole working day repeating one, often extremely simple, task. It was not surprising that they eventually rebelled; absenteeism increased, strikes became common and the manufacturers began to start thinking on other lines. These days very few assembly lines, unless the product is very simple, are entirely run by hand. Many types of line now exist which not only increase worker satisfaction but increase productivity too. Automation has changed the face of the assembly line. Many of the elementary tasks can now be carried out by machines which sort the components to be assembled and position them ready for fixing, either by machine or by hand.

The simplest improvement to the manual assembly line is the conveyor belt which moves the components and the evolving product rapidly down the line. From one of these conveyers a set of parts, possibly from a sub-assembly line, is picked up by the worker, plus maybe another from an adjacent bin and added to the main assembly. The semicompleted item is put on another conveyer and carried to the next stage of production.

Simple automation of the line replaces the manual labour by custom-built machines, with con-

Below: Radio-controlled Robocarriers, guided by lines embedded in the floor, move the part-completed bodies of Fiat's Uno between stations.

veyers moving assemblies from machine to machine. Personnel are still necessary though, mostly for quality control and routine inspection of the equipment. Such lines are mostly suitable for small products, manufactured in very large numbers. Human operators not only get bored with the trivial tasks involved at each stage of such manufacture but are physically unable to keep up with the required output rate, unless the line is duplicated expensively many times in one factory.

But ultimately such assembly lines are limited. They still incite boredom, eventually in the operatives that must man them, and if they are designed to produce, say, 2000 light bulbs an hour, that is just what they do, no more no less – and only one type of bulb. Flexibility in production rate and the ability of an assembly line to switch quickly from one type of product to a closely similar model are of paramount importance in today's changing world.

Nowadays, the design of a new product and the design of the assembly line which will produce it go hand in hand. Indeed, they are inseparable. Most products now are manufactured in a variety of colors and styles, or maybe with several optional extras or accessories and the assembly line must be able to handle any desired combination of these differences without stopping. Its rate of production must be flexible and the line must be designed so that it can run economically at several different output rates.

If the product is complex, large amounts of warehouse space may be needed to store the components before assembly. If the line cannot respond to changes in demand the finished product warehouse is either going to be half-empty (uneconomic from many points of view) or it will be full to bursting and unmanageable. Even if such a product and line can be designed to satisfy all these criteria, there is still the question of worker satisfaction to be taken into account. Absenteeism and strikes can wipe out all

Left: An assembly line at BAC's factory in Weybridge, Britain, producing front fuselage sections for Concorde. Below: Fiat's Uno is painted on a computer-controlled line at the company's Turin assembly plant. After an initial degrease by spray and immersion and several rinses with special surface activating chemicals, the body shell is coated with zinc and nickel phosphate and passivate. Then the paint is applied, ending with an enamel top coat.

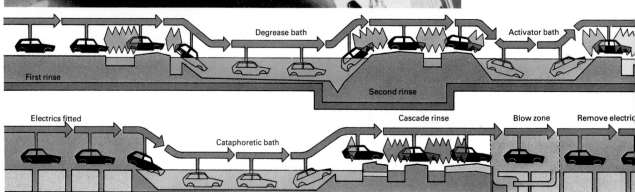

First rinse · Degrease bath · Second rinse · Activator bath

Electrics fitted · Cataphoretic bath · Cascade rinse · Blow zone · Remove electric

the financial and production benefits of a well designed production line if the people who must operate the system are not happy.

Several companies have experimented with new approaches to job satisfaction which involve novel ways of laying out the line. For instance, Volvo, the Swedish car manufacturer, has turned the concept of a *straight-through* line around so that each worker has a variety of tasks. Instead of moving the car under assembly progressively down a long line with each worker performing a boring job again and again, they have divided their work force up into teams which are responsible for assembling a whole car. In practice this meant totally changing the layout of the factory into a series of bays, rather than having a continuous line, each with its own assembly team and supply of components, possibly from sub-assembly lines.

The workers were retrained in a large variety of skills and trained to operate a rota system inside each group, so they do different jobs from week to week. Volvo found that productivity increased; there were less absenteeism and fewer strikes; the workers were happy – and they got paid more, since productivity had increased.

The productivity of an assembly line in economic terms is highly critical. Different arrangements of line may satisfy all the above conditions but still leave much to be desired economically.

Two key areas determine the economic viability of an assembly plant: the way in which the component parts (often manufactured by outside firms) are stored and supplied to the main line and the way in which the assembly equipment is maintained. Should the main line be halted for one shift in three for maintenance, or should there be a policy of training the operatives to maintain their own machines? A simple problem stated thus, but fraught with difficulty in practice, as objections are raised by a proliferation of unions and other interested parties.

In Japan

The problem of supplying the assembly line is neatly illustrated by the different approaches that

Above: A Fiat Uno body is assembled by four robot welders programed to remember every weld. The welding station can deal with two different body types, sliding a new set of holding clamps into position when the central computer requests.

have been taken by the U.S. and Japan.

The U.S. motor industry feels itself under siege by a Japanese industry capable of cheaper production costs and far higher quality control. In the U.S. it is significant that brought-in materials and components account for about half the manufacturing costs of an automobile, while in Japan the figure is about 70 per cent. By bringing the component vendor "into the family", insisting on, and collaborating on achieving, high product quality, and achieving a high level of vendor loyalty, the Japanese manufacturer is able to ensure that the suppliers produce exactly what he wants and when he wants it. Toyota, for instance, runs a very successful "just in time" system where components delivered to the factory go straight on to the assembly line, resulting

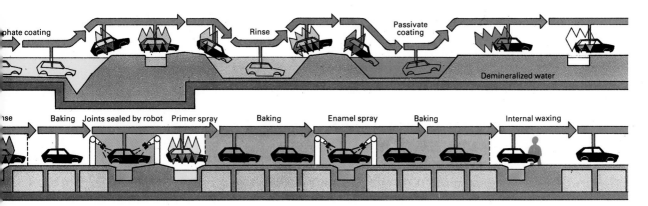

phate coating   Rinse   Passivate coating   Demineralized water

nse   Baking   Joints sealed by robot   Primer spray   Baking   Enamel spray   Baking   Internal waxing

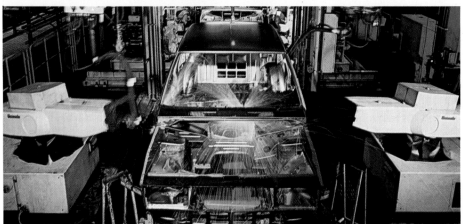

Industrial robots are versatile and apparently intelligent. Some, (far left), have eyes. Used to bolt hinges to doors, these employ a TV camera to direct the arm and hand. Other playback units (below left) can be taught a complex task like welding – the operator leading the robot through the motions and operations necessary for the job. Thus programed, it can perform the job repeatedly without error. The simplest robots are blind, deaf and dumb (above left) like this self-powered pallet controlled by a central production computer.

in cost savings to both Toyota and its suppliers, reduced inventories, less capital tied up in stock, no warehouses, uncluttered floor space and reduced labor costs.

The vendor, of course, bears the responsibility and risk of getting the logistics of supply exactly right. In effect, the component supplier takes over the warehousing and stock control functions from the main assembler. His reward is a close relationship with a major manufacturer. The U.S. supplier, on the other hand, is rewarded primarily for under-bidding his competitors. Often, Japanese firms will export their system to the U.S. when they set up production facilities in this country.

Within Japan, flow production of this sort has physical advantages in the older type of industry such as automobiles and steel production, where component parts are often bulky, making them difficult to store and retrieve easily, and is one reason for the vertical integration exemplified by the famous island steelworks in Tokyo harbor. This lands ore at one end while off-loading special steel products at the other – continuously. In the younger industries, such as electronics, the attractions of "just in time" inventories and exact supply quantities have not so much to do with the physical

flows – electronics parts tend to be very small and easily stored anyway – but have more to do with being able to change course, enabling new products to be introduced quickly without the need to use up expensive supplies of out of date components.

Competition in the Japanese home market, particularly for electronic hardware, is cut-throat, and hinges very strongly around price-cutting and a continuous turnover of new models in order to stay ahead. Large numbers of firms fall by the wayside. Those that survive move fast. "The nature of business is to make your own product obsolete", says Akio Morita, one of the founders of Sony. Long inventories would inhibit model changes and drive the slow movers out of business in a very short time.

Using computers

With the explosive development in computer science manufacturers now have the means to solve all their production problems in one fell swoop. Assembly lines can be devised which are run entirely by computers controlling industrial robots. Humans become virtually superfluous and the line can operate 24 hours a day without worker dissatisfaction. Mistakes can be made practically non-existent and by simply changing the control program different models can be produced on the same line simultaneously. The speed of production can also be made to match demand almost exactly.

Fiat, the Italian car manufacturer, has taken this technology to its logical conclusion. Several of their models are now produced almost entirely by robots in eerily deserted factories, where machines do all the hard work and the human operators work computer keyboards rather than noisy, smelly and dirty assembly line positions.

Flexibility

The whole production line was designed to achieve a very high level of flexibility, which meant very close liaison between the product design department and the production department. In designing each individual component, the engineer's primary objective was to design parts that were easy to assemble on automated production lines. The two processes had to be seen as complementary, allowing for future developments in directions as yet unknown. Robots are used throughout, since they can be reprogramed to perform a variety of tasks. This means less capital expenditure each time the line has to produce a new model, but this often meant that the engineers had to condense components that were previously separate. Fiat's Uno, for instance, is composed of only 172 major parts, 35 per cent fewer than their previous model, the 127, which itself only needed 267 parts.

Assembly starts with the chassis which consists of three major sub-assemblies, engine compartment, central floor and rear floor. The engine compartment like other major components is built on a totally automated line served by some twenty robots which weld the components automatically. Each chassis is then mounted on a pallet which slowly accumulates the whole car as it travels through the plant. Each pallet carries a computer identification code instructing the production line to supply the correct components. It determines, for instance, the final color, the optional extras specified in the order from the customer, the engine capacity and even the quality of the interior trim of the car.

As the car progresses through the factory, accumulating doors, engine paint, etc., the computer keeps track of exactly what is added to each protochassis; and it is all done by robots. In this way, completely different models can all be worked by the same production line. Each body is unique and the central computer takes care of its total assembly.

Such control over the details of the assembly procedure means the company can exploit sections of the market that previously would have been ignored. Robot and computer assembly processes thus benefit both consumer and manufacturer.

See also: Aerospace industry; Automobile; Computer; Conveyer; Robot, industrial; Warehousing.

Below: Contraceptive pill manufacture involves rigorous quality control and sophisticated packaging

• FACT FILE •

- The assembly line introduced by Henry Ford in 1913 was based on a combination of a railroad track manufacturing process and the overhead carcass trolleys of the Chicago meat factories. In 1912 Ford sold 82,000 Model Ts, but by 1919 monthly production was higher than this, culminating in a monthly record of 240,000 in November 1922.

- Completely automatic assembly lines use computer-based numerical control systems, in which robot movements have corresponding numerical values. These used to be fed to robots by means of perforated paper tapes, but can now be stored in computer programs, and changed to give an almost infinite range of tasks.

- The U.S. Air Force is building a factory where aircraft assembly will be carried out entirely by groups of robots working in separate cells. The robots, with built-in computer programs, will see and feel via TV camera eyes and electronic skins, in order to move around the cells completing their tasks. Some may even be able to communicate with one another.

Astronomical telescope

The invention of the optical telescope dates back to the pioneering days of science, when astronomers such as Galileo Galilei first gazed at the heavens in the early 1600s.

Telescopes collect more light than the human eye, so they can show objects that are too faint to be seen directly. Because they can magnify objects, telescopes show details too small to be visible to the unaided eye. For most modern astronomical purposes, the ability to gather light is more important than magnification. The means by which a telescope collects and focuses light is called its *objective*: the larger the objective, the more light the telescope can collect. A lens, called the eyepiece, magnifies the image formed by the objective. There are two principal types of astronomical telescopes: refractor telescopes and reflector telescopes.

Refractor telescopes

Some telescopes employ a lens as the objective, and these are called *refractor* telescopes. All early

Above: The great Andromeda galaxy through Britain's Schmidt telescope – effectively a large camera providing a wide-angle view of the heavens. Right: The Anglo-Australian reflecting telescope at Siding Spring, New South Wales, is ideally located away from the glare of city lights and polluted air – conditions that obscure faint astronomical objects. The main mirror, at the bottom of the main tube, is protected by a shutter of steel petals and the main tube swings on the horseshoe bearing mounted in the base.

Above: The high-altitude observatory at Pic du Midi, France, benefits from the thin, clear air.

refractors were plagued by optical defects, known as aberrations. Most serious were the fringes of color seen around an image, caused because a lens brings light of different wavelengths to a different focus. The resulting spread of colors that degrades an image is termed CHROMATIC ABERRATION.

Thin lenses with long focal length minimize chromatic aberration, but telescopes that employ such large lenses are immensely long and cumbersome, measuring 150 ft (46 m) or more in length. Suspended by a complex arrangement of poles and pulleys, these *aerial telescopes* were used to make important discoveries about the solar system, including Saturn's rings and several of its satellites.

Modern lenses are *achromatic* – producing a virtually color-free image. Such a lens is composed of two lenses, each of a different kind of glass so that the chromatic aberration of one lens cancels out that of the other. The invention of the achromatic lens led to the development of the 18.5 in. (0.47 m) refractor used to discover the tiny, faint, white dwarf star that accompanies Sirius. The two largest refractors ever built – and still in use today – are the 36 in. (0.91 m) of Lick Observatory and the 40 in. (1.01 m) of Yerkes Observatory – both American.

There is an upper limit to the size of a refractor, and the Yerkes telescope approaches that limit. The reason is that large lenses tend to sag because they are supported only around the edges. If a lens is made thicker to give it more strength, the glass absorbs some of the light passing through it thereby cancelling out the advantage of a larger aperture.

Fortunately a mirror, rather than a lens, can be used as an objective: and mirrors can be supported over their entire back surface. Thus the largest telescopes are all of this *reflector* type. Reflectors do not suffer from chromatic aberration, and are much more compact than refractors.

Reflector telescopes

The light collected by the main mirror of a reflector is focused on to a smaller, flat mirror, which diverts the light into an eyepiece placed at the side of the telescope tube. In other reflectors, the secondary mirror reflects the light back through a hole in the main mirror, where the eyepiece is placed. The secondary mirror blocks some of the incoming light from reaching the main mirror, but this is a minor disadvantage and does not affect the image.

Unlike a normal looking glass, in which the back surface is coated with a reflecting layer, a telescope mirror is coated on its front surface. This gives two advantages: the glass does not have to be optically perfect because light does not pass through it; and only one surface needs to be shaped and polished.

The first large telescope using a glass mirror was the 60 in. (1.5 m) reflector set up in 1908 on Mount Wilson, California, by George Ellery Hale. George Hale planned a giant 200 in. (5 m) reflector, which eventually opened on Palomar Mountain in 1948, ten years after his death.

For many years, the 200 in. (5 m) Hale reflector was the world's largest and most powerful optical telescope. It can provide magnified images at either a *Cassegrain focus* (at which the secondary mirror reflects light back through the main mirror) or at a *Coudé focus* (which lies adjacent to the main mirror). Conversion from one optical system to the other is simple and quick, making the telescope extremely versatile and adaptable.

Often, even the huge reflector of the Hale telescope might not collect sufficient light to give a clear, magnified image at either of these two focuses. A faint image becomes fainter as it is magnified, so the design of the Hale reflector enables an observer to sit also near the *principle focus* (which lies opposite the main mirror in the path of the incident light) and observe the unmagnified image. The disadvantage of placing the observer in the light path is greatly outweighed by the advantage of being able to observe a clearer image.

The largest optical telescope in the world is presently the 236 in. (6 m) at Zelenchukskaya in the Soviet Caucasus. Design problems with this telescope have meant that it has not yet taken its place among the ranks of the most powerful telescopes.

Large reflecting mirrors must have extremely smooth surfaces and this has made them prohibitively expensive. One solution is to assemble a number of smaller mirrors which are cheaper to make. The collecting area of a much larger telescope can then be mimicked. The largest telescope of this type is the Multiple Mirror Telescope or MMT of the University of Arizona. It has six 72 in. (1.8 m) mirrors with a combined collecting area equal to one 176 in. (4.5 m) diameter telescope.

Electronic IMAGE INTENSIFIERS are used to boost the faint light received from the most distant objects;

Right: The 150 in. (3.9 m) Anglo-Australian Telescope at Siding Spring Mountain, New South Wales. The open framework tube design is based on reflecting telescopes of similar size at Kitt Peak, Arizona, and Cerro Tololo, Chile. The main mirror has a focal ratio of f3.3, but there is a choice of secondary mirrors by which the final focal length can be varied. The telescope turns on two axes – the declination and polar – the latter rotating on a gigantic circular "horseshoe."

Above: The 157 in. (4 m) Cassegrain reflecting telescope of the Kitt Peak Observatory, Arizona.

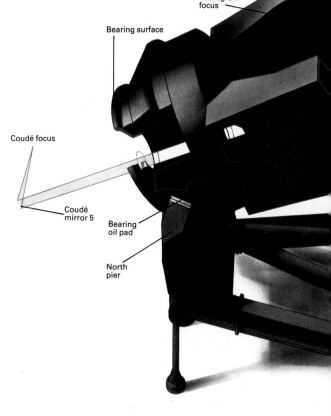

Adjus count

Decl axis

Primary mirror

Mirror supports

Cassegrain focus

Bearing surface

Coudé focus

Coudé mirror 5

Bearing oil pad

North pier

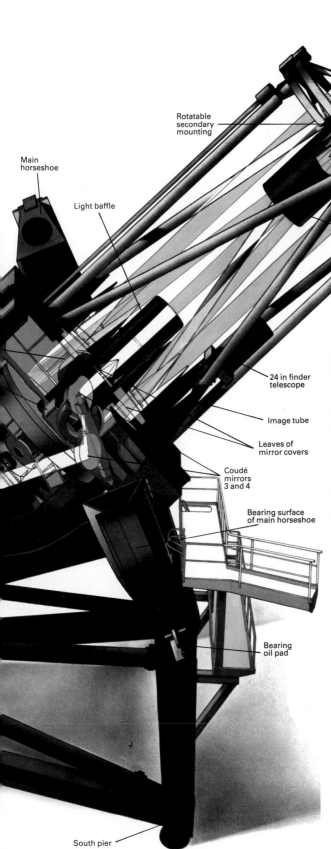

f15 Cassegrain secondary

Incoming light beam

Rotatable secondary mounting

f35 coude secondary mirror

Interchangeable end assembly

Leaves of mirror cover

Main horseshoe

Light baffle

Light baffle

24 in finder telescope

Image tube

Leaves of mirror covers

Coudé mirrors 3 and 4

Bearing surface of main horseshoe

Bearing oil pad

South pier

and computers are used to bring out otherwise imperceptible detail – a technique which is already bringing useful results.

The best view of the sky, however, is obtained above the blurring and filtering blanket of the Earth's atmosphere, out in space. Telescopes up to 32 in. (0.81 m) aperture have been flown in unmanned satellites, but in the late 1980s, a reflector known as the Space Telescope, with a mirror 94 in. (2.4 m) aperture, will be carried into orbit. The Space Telescope will show details 10 times as fine and objects 100 times as faint as the largest ground-based telescopes. It should answer many questions and give new clues to the origin of the universe.

Photographic telescopes

One drawback of conventional telescopes is that they allow only a small area of sky to be seen at a time. To overcome it, in 1930, an Estonian optician, Bernhard Schmidt, invented a new type of photographic telescope that combined lenses and mirrors to give a wide-angle view of the sky. Today, Schmidt telescopes are an essential part of observatories. Astronomers survey the sky with a Schmidt telescope before homing in on selected objects with their large reflectors.

Contrary to popular opinion, astronomers spend little time actually looking through telescopes. Usually, telescopes are used either as giant telephoto lenses to take long-exposure photographs that can reveal details far too faint to be seen by the eye alone, or they are attached to other instruments, such as *spectroscopes*.

See also: Astrophysics; Black hole; Image intensifier; Lens; Solar system; Space telescope.

Halfway to Heaven

Perched on the top of a mountain in mid-Atlantic, staring upward through an almost flawless lens composed entirely of air, the western world's latest observatory is all set to take a long, hard look through the window of our atmosphere and even into the Big Bang that started the universe. The Observatorio del Roque de los Muchachos, initiated by Britain's Royal Greenwich Observatory, is the highest point on La Palma, one of the Canary Islands. The center-piece of the observatory will be a new telescope, the fourth largest in the world. The 165 in. (4.2 m) William Herschel telescope, one of six that will eventually be built on the site, will be operated remotely from Britain.

The Herschel telescope will be a versatile precision instrument. The 165 in. (4.2 m) diameter light-collecting mirror is expected to surpass in its optical quality any large-scale terrestrial astronomical mirror, with 90 per cent of the light from a star falling within 0.5 arc sec. This specification of the telescope resolution is designed to match the expected seeing quality of the site. The accuracy of the paraboloidal surface is measured in millionths of an inch, and must be maintained even though the mirror would deform hundreds of times this amount under its own weight unless supported from below. So the mirror is supported by a flotation system of no less than 64 pneumatic pads. Thermal distortions produced in the mirror by temperature changes have been minimized by the use not of glass but of a ceramic materials of near-zero coefficient of expansion. Thus the mirror retains its critical shape at any temperature.

The tracking ability of the telescope will match the images produced in the telescope. If, as it follows stars rising and setting in their trip across the heavens, the telescope were to waver, the star images which it produces will be noticeably asymmetrical when recorded in the hour-long time-exposures necessary to detect the faintest stars, and this affects measurements of their brightness and position. The amount of tracking error allowed in the Herschel telescope is 0.05 arc sec, equivalent to following the nose on the head of a president on a 1 in. (2 cm) coin at a distance of 2½ miles (4 km), if the coin is moved at 0.6 mph (1 km/hr).

The telescope will track the stars using an altazimuth mounting, in which the two axes of rotation on which the telescope moves are horizontal (*alt*itude axis) and vertical (*azi*muth axis). Conventional telescopes are equatorially mounted, or tilted

so that the vertical axis is aligned with the polar axis of rotation of the Earth. These telescopes track stars by rotation about this this axis alone: the altazimuth mounting (used for the Soviet 240 in. (6 m) telescope and the Multi Mirror telescope in Arizona) is far more complex because motion in the two axes has to be synchronized closely; but because one axis is parallel to the force of gravity, the telescope is symmetrical, more compact, more economical, more rigid and of higher performance.

The telescope is designed with a *prime focus*, at the focus of the 165 in. (4.2 m) diameter f/2.5 mirror. Although the images of stars on the axis of the parabolic mirror are theoretically perfect, the mirror design is such that aberrations quickly make the off-axis star images exceed the seeing size. A three-element lens has been designed to correct these aberrations and over a ½° arc (the same as the Moon, when seen from Earth) the telescope will

Above: The 165 in. (4.2 m) main mirror being polished. The mirror is made from a ceramic material with no coefficient of thermal expansion and is supported by 64 pneumatic pads to prevent it from collapsing under its own weight.

yield images at the prime focus which are smaller than the seeing size.

This means the telescope can photograph a comparatively large area of the sky. This use of the telescope will, however, be comparatively rare. The camera holding photographic detectors and the triplet corrector lens will be dismounted and replaced by a second convex mirror which will refocus the starlight and direct it back toward the primary mirror to a choice of four focuses selected with a movable flat mirror. One focus, the Cassegrain focus, will be through a hole in the primary mirror; most of the time a spectrograph will be mounted

here to analyze starlight by splitting it into its constituent wavelengths. The distribution of starlight in a spectrum gives information about the star's composition and physical state as well as its velocity.

The telescope beam can also be turned by a right angle through the altitude axis of the telescope to one of two Nasmyth focuses on each side of the telescope. Two platforms fixed here will carry large instruments, like a high resolution spectrograph to study the light of the brighter stars in greater detail than the lower resolution spectrograph at the Cassegrain focus. Brighter stars can be studied when the Moon is up, a time when fainter stars are lost in the flood of moonlight over the night sky. When the Moon sets in the course of a night, the flat mirror can be used to switch the telescope beam from the high resolution spectrograph at the Cassegrain focus to study faint ones.

Already on the La Palma observatory site, Britain has built a 98 in. (2.5 m) telescope and a 40 in. (1 m) telescope to provide the full range of telescope sizes necessary at a modern observatory.

The 98 in. (2.5 m) telescope is the Isaac Newton telescope formerly at the Royal Greenwich Observatory in Herstmonceux, Sussex. This telescope has been furnished with a new mirror and a modern control system as well as a suite of up-to-date instruments, including an Image Photon Counting System (IPCS). The latter is a TV camera system equipped with an image intensifier which amplifies light ten million times. Having traveled from distant faint stars, individual photons energize single electrons in the sensitive detecting layer (photocathode) of this device; the electrons are accelerated by a high voltage in progressive amplification stages and at the final stage produce a splash of light for each photon detected in the first stage. This splash of light is recorded by the TV camera, recognized as arising from one photon and counted in a computer to form an image.

The Image Photon Counting System has been used to record the spectra of faint quasars at huge distances: light from the most distant has traveled across the Universe for 10 thousand million years. It has also revealed absorption lines in the spectra of distant quasars caused by material between the quasar and us – primordial hydrogen created by the Big Bang at the start of the Universe about 13 thousand million years ago. This material is a fossil from the Big Bang and a major source of information to us about conditions at the start of the Universe. Other absorption lines are caused by the halos of extremely faint galaxies which are too faint to be seen directly but appear in silhouette against the distant quasar.

Astrophysics

Astrophysics is the physics of astronomy – it attempts to explain the objects seen in the sky in terms of the laws of physics that apply on Earth.

Almost all the information about the stars, planets and cosmic bodies comes in the form of radiation – usually thought of as light, but including radio waves, X RAYS, and the rest of the spectrum of ELECTROMAGNETIC RADIATION. The only exceptions to this are Moon samples, meteorites and cosmic rays – high energy charged particles from space. These can be analyzed chemically.

Physical observing methods

The astronomical telescope collects light from objects which may well be so faint that they are invisible to the naked eye. Photography makes even fainter objects visible by collecting their light over periods of an hour or longer. A photographic plate registers only about one light particle, or photon, in every hundred. Nowadays much of astronomy is carried out using electronic detectors called CCDs (Charge Coupled Devices) which can normally detect over fifty per cent of incident light. But the addition of the SPECTROSCOPE to these has made it possible to analyze the light from stars.

The spectroscope splits light into its individual wavelengths, or spectrum. Each chemical element has its own characteristic spectrum. Starlight has a *continuous spectrum*, with all the colors of the rainbow, crossed by dark lines where particular wavelengths have been absorbed by gases in the outer layers of the star. By comparing the wavelengths of these lines with those produced by gases on Earth, it is possible to discover what elements are present in the star, their quantities and temperatures.

Each star has a predominant color, which depends on its surface temperature. Red stars are cool, as low as 5400° F (3000° C), while the hottest stars are blue, about 45,000° F (25,000° C). The Sun's surface temperature is about 10,472° F (5800° C).

The DOPPLER shift of the lines shows whether a star is moving towards or away from the Earth and at what speed. In the case of a double star where two stars can be seen orbiting each other, this indicates the sizes of their orbits and can be used to discover the masses of the stars by KEPLER's and NEWTON's LAWS. Since the speed of the stars in their orbits and the time taken to go around are both known it is possible to calculate the actual diameters of their orbits. These diameters can also be measured as small angles in the sky, from which the distance of the stars from Earth can be calculated.

The distance of the nearby stars can be found by observing the small shift in their positions as the Earth circles the Sun – in effect giving a stereo view

Above: The neutrino experiment consisted mainly of a 119,000 gallon (450,000 litre) tank of cleaning fluid in a South Dakota gold mine to detect the emission rate of neutrinos from the Sun.

of the sky. This shift is known as the star's *parallax*.

When a star's distance is known, it is possible to decide how bright it is compared with, say, the Sun. The Sun is found to be about midway between the brightest and faintest stars.

How stars shine

From the stars' spectra, it has been found that the main elements in stars are the gases hydrogen and helium; furthermore the stars are producing vast amounts of energy. The source of this energy was a mystery until Einstein suggested in his RELATIVITY THEORY that MATTER itself could be transformed into ENERGY. It is thought that the Sun and stars are powered by nuclear FUSION reactions, in which energy is produced by the conversion of hydrogen into helium, deep in their interiors.

Because the brightest stars are using their hydrogen supply very rapidly, they cannot continue to shine brightly for more than a few million years. The blue stars are therefore the youngest that can be observed. The younger, more recent stars are found to contain more of the elements heavier than helium than the old stars. This is because the heavier elements can only be produced at very high temperatures inside very massive stars. These stars become unstable because eventually they cannot produce energy to support their outer layers and they explode. These events are known as *supernovas*. The explosion distributes the elements throughout space, and when a new star forms it will

Left: The Horsehead Nebula, in Orion. The color effect is produced by combining three photographs, each taken through a different color filter. To the left of the Horsehead are two bluish nebulae lit by two stars embedded in clouds of dust and gas. Below left: The Crab Nebula formed by a supernova in 1054. The event was witnessed by the Ancient Chinese, but today it can be seen through simple telescopes. A radio image (below) shows that there is intense emission at the center of the nebula while it continues to expand producing not only light but copious amounts of radiation.

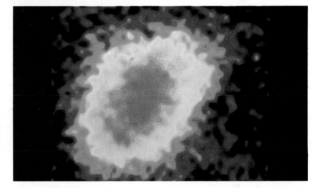

have a certain proportion of heavier elements in it.

The formation process of a star has never been observed, but it is thought that a mass of gas contracts and begins to heat up by the friction of the gas particles colliding with each other. If the gas cloud was rotating slowly to start with, it will spin faster, just as a skater spins faster when the arms are brought closer to the body. The rotation speed may become sufficiently high that a disk of the material is thrown off. This could condense to form the small dense bodies called planets. Consequently, the elements found on Earth, including those that humans are made from, were originally created deep inside massive stars.

Some supernovas leave behind very dense remnants, only a few miles in diameter, rotating several times a second. These give out pulses of energy, mostly of radio waves, and are called *pulsars*. They represent matter in the most highly condensed form known.

Nebulae and galaxies

Apart from stars, telescopes show small hazy patches in the sky called *nebulae* – Latin for clouds. The spectroscope shows that some of these are the clouds of gas and dust out of which stars form. Others, which often appear spiral, are actually distant *galaxies*, each containing thousands of millions of stars, and very far away – the nearest is at a distance of 12 million million million miles.

At great distances in the universe are found *quasars*. These appear to be single points of light, yet they send out more energy than a whole galaxy. It is possible that they represent the early stages of galaxies. When astronomers observe the most distant quasars they are looking at the universe when it was only one-fifth of its present age of fifteen billion years. Since light travels at a limited speed, the radiation from these objects must have left them thousands of millions of years ago. Quasars are thought to be at the heart of galaxies whose stars are too faint to discern. All galaxies may go through a violent quasar phase in their youth.

See also: Astronomical telescope; Black hole; Electromagnetic radiation; Fusion; Matter.

Atom and molecule

The word atom is derived from the Greek word *atomos* which means indivisible. The Greek Philosopher Democritus, in the fifth century BC, first suggested that the whole of the material world might be assembled from a basic building block, the atom. Nineteenth century chemists found more than one type of atom. Today we know of 92 naturally occurring types, or ELEMENTS, and a further fourteen which have been synthesized by man.

The nineteenth century Russian chemist, Dmitri Mendeleev, was the first to arrange elements into groups with similar properties. He noticed that, for example, the elements lithium, sodium and potassium underwent similar chemical reactions. Here was a hint of structure on an even more elementary, subatomic scale.

By the beginning of the twentieth century the atom had lost its claim to be nature's fundamental building block. In 1897 J. J. Thomson at Cambridge University discovered the ELECTRON, a particle almost 2000 times lighter than hydrogen, the lightest element. Later, in 1913, the New Zealander, Ernest Rutherford, found that the atom possessed an ultracompact core of NUCLEUS.

The picture of the atom that emerged in the early decades of the twentieth century was of a tiny nucleus containing about ninety-nine per cent of the MASS of the atom, surrounded by a cloud of negatively charged electrons. The nucleus contains positively charged PROTONS and neutral particles called NEUTRONS. The electromagnetic attraction between opposite charges – the negative electrons and the equal number of positive protons – binds the atom together.

A typical atom is about three hundred millionths of an inch across. If its nucleus were the size of a tennis ball, the atomic diameter would be just over half a mile. So, Rutherford's remarkable discovery was that atoms are almost entirely empty space.

In the lightest atom, hydrogen, one electron orbits a solitary proton in the nucleus. In the next heaviest, helium, two electrons orbit a nucleus containing two protons and two neutrons. Neutrons help prevent the electrical repulsion between protons from breaking the nucleus apart. And so on up to uranium, the heaviest naturally occurring element with ninety-two protons, ninety-two electrons and over one hundred and forty neutrons.

The modern description of the inside of the atom arose in the 1920s with the development of QUANTUM

Below: Using the simple rules that control how atoms link, researchers can model new molecules.

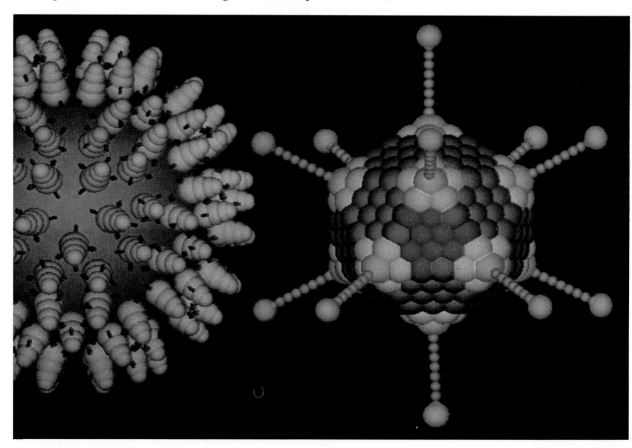

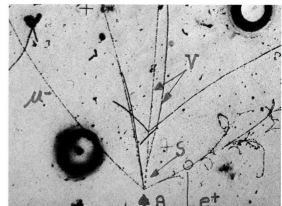

Above: The Super Proton Synchrotron at CERN, the European center for atomic research, has a ring of 960 magnets to focus and direct particle beams.

MECHANICS by the Danish physicist, Niels Bohr and others. In this picture the electron of a hydrogen atom is confined to a region of space around the nucleus called an *atomic orbital*. This is not an orbit like that of a planet around the Sun. The negative charge of the electron must be thought of as smeared throughout the region. Quantum theory predicts that the electron may only occupy a limited set of allowed orbitals. To move from one orbital to another the electron must either absorb or emit a PHOTON, or light particle.

These allowed orbitals can be regarded as being arranged in *shells* around the nucleus. In atoms with many electrons the electrons populate the innermost shells first. No two electrons are permitted to share the same orbital. It is the outermost electrons, those outside completed shells, which determine the chemical properties of elements. These electrons participate in bonds with other atoms to form MOLECULES. Lithium, sodium and potassium all have a lone outer electron, explaining why Mendeleev grouped them together. Elements such as helium have all their electrons in completed shells and so do not react with other atoms; they are inert.

A molecule of a substance is the smallest arrangement of atoms that can exist under normal conditions. A helium molecule is simply a helium atom. But an oxygen molecule is a pair of oxygen atoms bound together. And a water molecule is an oxygen atom bound to two hydrogen atoms. Large ORGANIC MOLECULES like the proteins which form our body may contain many thousands of linked atoms

The forces which bind atoms into molecules, like the forces that hold atoms together are electrical in nature. A simple way of describing intermolecular forces is the following: when two atoms are separated by a large distance they see each other as neutral and there is no attraction between them.

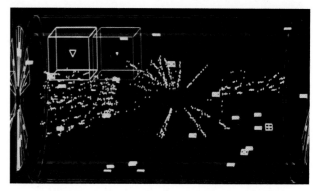

Top: Particle tracks in a bubble chamber show that when a neutrino (A) hits a nucleon, a muon (μ^-), a positron (e+), and an uncharged particle (S) are produced. S then decays into charged particles. Similar reactions can be modeled (above) by computer, then analyzed.

But, if they are brought close together they distort each others charge distribution and attract each other. If they are pushed closer still the negative electron clouds will overlap and strongly repel each other. And so the normal intermolecular spacing is the separation between atoms where the attractive and repulsive forces are balanced.

In practise their are several distinct types of electrical bonds which give rise to the situation just described. In a very common one, the COVALENT BOND, electrons are shared between two or more atoms. For example, the two hydrogen nuclei in a hydrogen molecule share their electrons. In effect the electron cloud encompasses the pair of positive nuclei. The resulting molecule has its own orbitals where electrons are allowed just like an atom although the quantum mechanical description is now slightly more complicated. The covalent bond between carbon atoms can create long chains of carbon atoms that are the essential components of our bodies.

See also: Bond, chemical; Compound; Element, chemical; Energy; Matter; Particle accelerator.

Atomic clock

The very accurate measurement of time is important in many areas of modern technology, such as space exploration, satellite tracking, navigation, and scientific research; since the mid 1950s this has been provided by scientific instruments known as atomic clocks.

Modern precision time systems are based on the simpler quartz clock which depends on the steady rate of vibration of a quartz crystal to keep it accurate. The frequency of the quartz crystal vibrations will, however, gradually alter over a period of time and need readjusting. In order to set a quartz clock to an exact frequency, an accurate frequency standard must be available for comparison, and this is obtainable from an atomic clock.

There is very little resemblance between an atomic clock and a normal one. It has no clock face, digital or audible read-out normally associated with recording the time. It does not, therefore, tell the time, but provides a reference standard frequency which is used to calibrate other clocks. An atomic clock looks rather like a complex piece of laboratory equipment with vacuum pumps and electronic apparatus surrounding it.

Principles of the atomic clock

All atoms in their natural state emit and absorb pulses, or quanta, of energy, owing to the switching back and forth of ELECTRONS from one orbit, or energy

Below: The U.S. Naval Observatory atomic clock is accurate to within one thousandth of a second a year. Such clocks are the basis of timekeeping.

level, around the central NUCLEUS to another. When an electron changes from a high energy orbit to a lower energy orbit a pulse of electromagnetic radiation or PHOTON is emitted, and the frequency of this radiation increases proportionally to the change in energy. Conversely, to boost an electron from a low to a higher energy state, a photon must be fed into the electron from an outside source. The energy change is proportional to the radiation frequency.

These energy levels of an atom are more constant than any other known natural phenomenon, not varying with temperature, pressure or gravity, and are therefore ideally suited to determining standard frequencies. Certain elements such as the alkali metals caesium and rubidium, and hydrogen are especially useful for this work. They have only one electron in their outer orbit to emit and absorb energy, and their respective frequencies are relatively uncomplicated and easier to use than those from atoms with more electrons in this orbit.

The caesium clock

A caesium atom can be at one of two energy states depending on whether the outer electron is spinning in the same or opposite sense to that of the nucleus. These different states influence the path of a free caesium atom as it travels through a magnetic field.

Furthermore, if a caesium atom passes through an electromagnetic field which has a frequency equivalent to the difference between the caesium atom's two energy states, the atom will be induced to change from one state to the other. If a beam of caesium atoms is passed through such a field then the maximum number of state transitions will occur when the field frequency is tuned precisely to the natural frequency of the caesium. The caesium clock measures indirectly the number of transitions that occur and constantly tries to achieve the greatest possible number by means of a feedback circuit to the field frequency controller. The field frequency is therefore locked on to the caesium frequency, and by suitable electronic division of this very high frequency to a manageable rate, it can be used to control the accuracy of a quartz clock.

In practice, the method by which this is done is to heat caesium, which has a very low melting point, in a small electric oven set inside a straight tube from which all the air has been removed by vacuum pumps. Atoms stream out of a slit in the front of the oven and down the tube – there is no air to slow their progress. On the way they pass a magnet which deflects atoms in one state to one side, and atoms in the other state to the other side. This has the effect of deflecting some atoms way off axis but focussing the rest into a converging beam.

The beam converges on a cavity resonator, a hollow antenna-like device which passes an electromagnetic field across it. This field is kept at a fre-

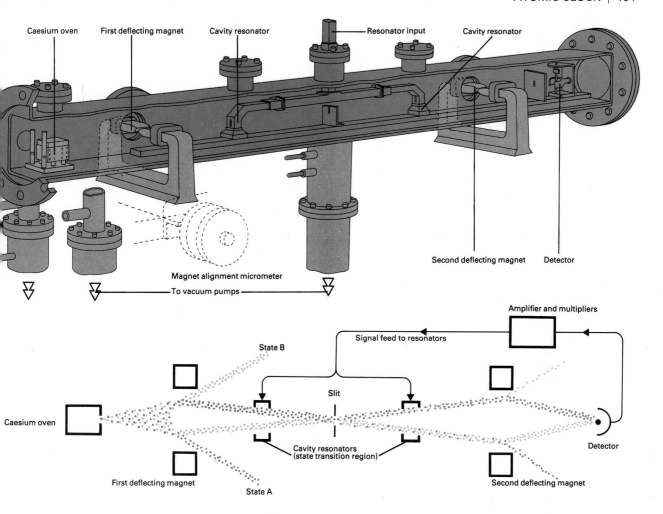

Top: An atomic beam chamber showing the caesium oven, the deflecting magnets, cavity resonators and detector. Above: The operating principle of the atomic clock relies on feedback; a general term for the return of an output signal to its input in order to modify its characteristics.

quency of 9192 MHz (millions of cycles a second) by electronically multiplying the 5 MHz signal from a quartz clock. Provided that the quartz clock is running at exactly the right frequency, the field will change the spin direction of nearly all the atoms passing through it, but without affecting the tidy focusing of the beam in which they travel.

The beam comes to a focus at a narrow slit in the middle of the resonator, which stops any off-course atoms. The beam spreads out on the other side of the slit, but the focusing has made it cross over, and an atom that was on the left side of the beam before the slit is on the right side after it.

At the same time the resonator has changed the spin direction of nearly all the atoms. Since atoms in one state are on one side of the beam (and vice versa) the net result is that the two changes cancel

each other out, and the beam emerges from the resonator with atoms in a particular state on the same side as when they entered.

The beam then passes through a second magnet, which focuses it to strike a detecting device at the end of the tube. The few atoms that have not changed their state are on the wrong side of the beam to be focused, and are thrown out to one side. The atoms striking the detector cause it to emit a signal which is fed back to the quartz clock.

If the frequency of the quartz clock slips a little, the frequency of the resonator in the tube is no longer 9192 MHz and the spin direction of the atoms is not changed. As a result, all the atoms emerging from the resonator are on the wrong side of the beam to be focused onto the detector. None of them strikes it, and the absence of any signal causes the quartz clock to change its frequency until it receives the signal again. Although other forms of atomic clock are in use throughout the world, the caesium clock provides the basis of most of the present international measurements of time.

See also: Atom and molecule; Electron; Time.

Audio-visual

Audio-visual is used at all levels of education from the classroom through to industrial training in order to make instruction and the dissemination of information to large groups more effective.

A wide variety of equipment is now available for this, which permits new forms of expression and instruction, with and without a teacher or demonstrator being present.

The simplest form of audio-visual is also one of the oldest – a chalkboard and a teacher. Modern educational pressures, however, demand increasing efficiency in presenting information. Writing on a chalkboard requires time, slows the learning process and, for effective communication, requires a fair degree of skill on the part of the teacher. Many instructors still continue to use the chalkboard, however, and would not be without it – others rely to a greater and greater extent upon the overhead projector and screen.

The overhead projector

This is a simple device, consisting of a box which contains a powerful light source, with a transparent top surface or platen. Prepared semitransparent drawings or models are placed on the platen. Alternatively, a continuous roll of transparent material such as acetate sheet, which is arranged to be passed across the illuminated area from one roller to another, may be used. Information is written on this material with a suitable pen. An image of the platen area is projected by means of a lens assembly and mirror on to a screen placed behind the projector. The mirror and lens unit is usually supported on a vertical pillar at one corner of the box; it can be

Below: This special mounting combines a slide and half a minute of sound effects or commentary.

Above: The overhead projector is often preferred to chalkboard and chalk, particularly if large amounts of information or diagrams can be prepared for showing before the lecture. Right: Video tape is cheap and flexible and it can be edited easily to produce highly polished presentations.

adjusted for sharp focusing.

The advantage of this form of aid is that the teacher faces the audience and the picture is thrown over his or her shoulder on to a screen behind. With hand drawn material the themes of a subject may be developed at the instructor's own pace. Professionally prepared material is also available covering a wide variety of subjects. In some instances, a basic transparency (accurately located on the platen) is supplemented with added overlays that are flipped into position in sequence.

Working models, consisting of thin flat components (often cut from transparent or translucent plastic sheet) add interest to a presentation. Typical examples are mechanisms showing the function of a car engine, meshing gear wheels and so on.

Movie projectors

Although the overhead projector is now widely used, the movie projector has actually been established longer in many schools and training establishments. The commonest size of film is 16 mm but a narrow size, standard 8 mm and, recently, the improved Super 8 is now finding increasing favor. In general, the 8 mm gauge is less expensive than 16 mm, and the equipment is lighter and more compact. Although there are still some silent films available, the majority of films are now accompanied by a sound track.

The commonest form of machine is mounted

firmly upon a stand and projects its image in a darkened room, with the loudspeaker contained within the projector or, alternatively, placed close to the screen, in front of the audience. For individual or small group instruction, compact projectors are available. These are usually self-contained, suitcase type units and have a small translucent screen onto which the film is back-projected.

For the larger type of projector the film is supplied on reels or spools, but for the compact types the film is more often supplied in cassettes. These are sealed plastic boxes which protect the film from mishandling, finger marks and dust. They slide easily into the projector and do not require any manipulative skill on the part of the user. Recent introductions in this field include 8 mm film which contains both still and motion picture material, linked with magnetic tape tracks which provide audio information and control the film speed.

Still projectors

The filmstrip or slide projector shows individual pictures in sequence. Filmstrips may be produced on 35 or 16 mm width material. They have the advantages of being light, strong and inexpensive, with a picture sequence which can not be disarranged. Slides are generally made to the international 50 mm square standard outline and these contain a picture area of 24 x 36 mm, horizontal or upright, placed centrally in the slide. Other bigger sizes of slide are available for professional use in large scale presentations. Filmstrips and slides in color are now most commonly used instead of those in black and white.

Filmstrips, slide and motion picture materials are nationally and internationally standardized through the British Standards Institution, the American National Standards Institute and the International Organization for Standardization so that they are globally interchangeable.

It is common practice to link both filmstrips and slides with a sound accompaniment. The sound is usually recorded on magnetic tape, frequently in cassette form. This type of sound cassette contains a narrow width tape having two separate tracks. One of these carries the commentary, music and effects, while the second track carries the magnetic instructions which control the picture change. In advanced forms, two projectors may be linked together so that a picture from one of them appears to dissolve into the picture from the other. The rate of change is controlled by the information encoded on the second track of the tape.

Having established a basic principle of dual projectors, sound accompaniment and control track, it is a logical step forward to a number of pairs of projectors. Such assemblies are often used in multi-screen or multiimage presentations of considerable complexity in which the audience is wholly involved, since both images and sound can be

Above: In this college students can play back a range of videotapes prepared by the academic staff, stopping on a single frame or replaying part of a tape at will. Right: A specialist self-contained unit for viewing slide presentations in daylight.

designed to provide a display of continuing interest.

Television and video tape recording

Television techniques have provided one of the more important advances in the audio-visual field. TV is used, for example, in schools, universities and in industry, in the form of closed circuit television (CCTV). This is a much more localized system than is used in normal broadcasting, because the camera and receiver (the set or monitor) are directly connected by a cable and no transmissions over the air take place.

CCTV has the advantage over movie film that the results are seen immediately – the images do not have to be processed.

The television camera, providing either black and white or color pictures, is small, compact and easy to operate. The real skill lies in the actual production of the audio-visual program.

It is common practice to link closed circuit television with a videotape recorder (VTR) so that the images seen by the television camera are recorded on magnetic tape (often on cassette) in the same way that sound is stored on a conventional tape recorder. In professional broadcasting, 2 in. (50 mm) wide tape is used. In education it is more common to use 1 in. (25 mm) or ½ in. (12.5 mm) wide tapes, which give a lower, but still acceptable picture quality. Later developments have shown that it is possible to record picture and sound on tape as narrow as ¼ in. (6 mm) – the width used on standard home audio recorders.

The combination of closed circuit television and VTR has proved to be a powerful audio-visual aid.

Immediate playback of a training session, for example, allows students to study their own behavior. In demonstrations and lectures, the camera can show to a large audience experiments or events which could otherwise have only been seen by a few people.

Further, university lectures can benefit greatly by being prerecorded since the lecturer can produce a much more polished presentation.

Many countries now use over-the-air broadcasting for educational programs, which are taken as part of school lessons. Apart from the obvious point that pupils would prefer to watch TV than listen to their teacher, this brings a wide range of visual resources into the classroom – language classes can effectively be presented from the foreign country, for example. In Britain, the *Open University* exists to provide a university degree to correspondent students through programs broadcast on the national radio and television networks.

A recent development, though one which is already becoming widespread, is the use of video cassettes. Using ½ in. (12.5 mm) or ¾ in. (18 mm) tape in book-sized cassettes, they can give up to six hours' playing time in black and white or color. Recordings can be made almost as easily as with a sound-only tape recorder, and a player unit will replay the cassette through a TV set.

These cassettes have many applications in industry, particularly as sales aids and as a general means of communication and entertainment.

See also: Magnetic tape; Movie production; Tape recorder; Video camera; Video recording.

Autoclave

The autoclave is a pressure vessel used in hospitals for sterilizing surgical instruments, dressings, bedding, rubber gloves, or any other materials required to be free from bacterial or similar contamination. They are widely used in medical and dental clinics, surgeries and operating rooms, veterinary clinics and intensive care units.

Such microorganisms can be killed by prolonged dry heat, but sterilization is achieved much more rapidly in the autoclave by treating its contents with moist steam under pressure, at a high temperature. Increased pressure has no direct effect on micro organisms, but allows steam to be used at a temperature well above that of boiling water. On contacting the material to be sterilized the steam condenses, giving up some of its heat and raising the temperature of the materials. Once the material reaches steam temperature, no further condensation will take place, and temperature equilibrium is reached. If the temperature is too high, superheated or dry steam will be produced and moisture will be evaporated from the material in the autoclave, resulting in much less efficient sterilization. Consequently, temperature and pressure are carefully controlled to maintain optimum conditions.

A typical autoclave consists of a large cylindrical pressure vessel, up to 20 ft (6 m) long, and 6 ft (2 m) in diameter. This is closed with a pressure-tight door through which articles to be sterilized are loaded, packed in containers which allow free circulation of steam. Air is pumped out to produce a near vacuum, then steam is fed in from an external boiler supply. This process ensures almost instant penetration of steam into porous materials, which might otherwise not reach a high enough internal temperature. When nonporous materials are to be sterilized, air may be flushed out with steam, rather than by using the vacuum technique. To reduce sterilization time when large loads are being processed, the material is sometimes preheated with a flow of steam before the final vacuum and steam sterilization cycle takes place.

Pressure builds up until the required working temperature is reached; for example, a pressure of 15 psi (one atmosphere) results in a temperature of 250° F (121° C), which would be maintained for 15 minutes or more to effect sterilization. A timing device locks the autoclave door, preventing removal of material before completion of the sterilization cycle. When sterilization is complete, steam is pumped out, and the autoclave allowed to cool. Cooling results in a pressure drop within the autoclave, and filtered air must be admitted before it can be opened. Additional safety features mean that the elements cannot be energized with the door open. A

boil-dry cut-out prevents overheating and a safety valve operates if the chamber reaches a pressure of about 36 psi (2.45 bar).

In hospitals, jacketed autoclaves are often used. After sterilization, high temperature steam is fed into the jacket around the pressure vessel, and dries the contents by driving off moisture. In large units, and for industrial use, the entire process can be automated. Goods to be sterilized are prepacked in suitable containers, loaded on a roller track, and fed automatically to the autoclave. An inverted pressure vessel is lowered over the containers and is sealed by a gasket before the sterilizing cycle takes place. The pressure vessel is then raised, and the container moves off on the roller track.

Autoclaves are also used for the heat stabilization of synthetic fabrics, to minimize subsequent shrinking. Other types are used for impregnation of timber, the vacuum cycle forcing a preservative into the wood. The term autoclave is sometimes also used to describe a high pressure reaction vessel.

See also: Pressure; Temperature; Vacuum.

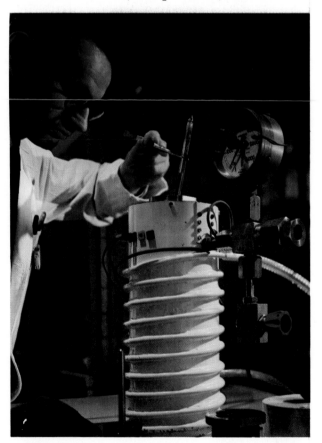

Above: A portable autoclave, capable of working at 608° F (320° C) and 4000 psi (278 bar), being tested by completely dissolving a sample, contained in a silica tube, in a suitable liquid medium.

Autogiro

An autogiro is an aircraft which derives its lift from an unpowered rotor system mounted above the machine, with blades rotating horizontally.

Autogiros differ from helicopters in that their rotor blades are driven by the air flowing upwards past them (the principle being known as *autorotation*), whereas the helicopter has mechanically driven blades set at a greater *pitch angle*, so as to screw upwards through the air.

To take off, maintain height, or climb an autogiro needs an engine and a propeller to drive it forwards. By tilting the lift rotor system slightly backwards, the rotor blades will lift the aircraft, even though the air flows up and through the rotor. A simple autogiro needs some forward speed to maintain height, so unlike the helicopter, it cannot hover or take off vertically – its greatest limitation.

Autorotation

The motion of the rotor and the resulting upward thrust, or lift, depend entirely upon autorotation resulting from the air flowing up and through the slightly tilted rotor blades as the machine moves forward through the air.

Nature has applied the principle of autorotation for millions of years, seen in the whirling flight of a sycamore seed as it falls to the ground. Autorotation slows its descent and the wind has greater opportunity to disperse the seeds over a wider area.

The windmill was probably the first human invention which used autorotation, by harnessing the wind to produce rotary motion. The idea of a flying windmill, where rotating sails produced a wind to lift the machine, had a certain fascination

Below: Having characteristics of both fixed and rotary wing flying, the autogiro allows previous flying experience from either field to be applied.

for inventors, and among Leonardo da Vinci's thousands of drawings is an idea for flight along these lines. The real possibility for achieving such a machine was, however, delayed until the development of the AIRFOIL and the airplane some four hundred years later.

A windmill is basically an airscrew or propeller working in reverse, such that the air flowing over the sails is deflected by them, and exerts a force on the sails pushing them round. The sails effectively give way to the wind and are pushed round by it.

As early as the Middle Ages, however, it was realized that if the sails were set at a very flat angle to the wind they would be made to rotate against the airflow and thus be pulled round into the wind. The principle here is the same as with a sailing ship which can tack close to the wind, meaning it can move forward against the wind, at a shallow angle to it, if the sails are properly set. In much the same way a glider moves forward as it descends.

The rotor blades of an autogiro are shaped to achieve the same effect, and set at a shallow angle of about 3° to the horizontal plane in which they rotate. The shape is that of an airfoil which enables the blades to turn into the airflow rather than be pushed round by it. This is basically what allows an autogiro to fly.

When turning fast these rotor blades offer considerable resistance to the upward airflow, and it is this resistance that can be used to provide lift. The amount of lift created depends upon a compromise between the airspeed of the rotors and the resistance the rotating blades offer to the airflow past them. In practice, the desired lifting force is only produced when the blade speed greatly exceeds the forward speed of the machine.

The advancing blade bends upwards in the airstream to store energy which it releases by springing back downwards as it retreats.

Take off

For take off, the rotor must produce adequate lift and it is necessary, therefore, to bring the rotor up to the required speed. This can be done in two ways.

The first and simplest way is to propel the machine forwards and, by tilting back the rotor system, use the airflow through the blades to build up the rotor speed. This, however, requires a suitably long runway. The second method involves more complex machinery but makes possible very short take off distances. Here the rotor is brought up to speed by a linkage to the engine used to provide the forward motion. When the rotor has the correct speed, the linkage is disengaged. The machine is then allowed to move forward, and take off is achieved by tilting back the rotor system. Some autogiros can jump-start by overspeeding the rotor using the engine. The drive is then dis-

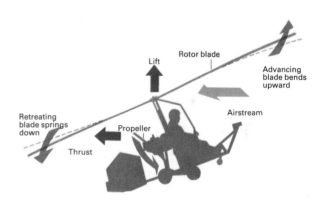

Top: The controls are of the utmost simplicity.
Above: Lift is created by the spinning rotor and the autogiro must move forward to take off.

engaged, and the rotor pitch increased. The aircraft jumps, using the stored energy, and continues then in autorotation.

Landing

When the engine and propeller speed are reduced, the forward speed decreases and the autogiro goes into a steady descent path. The autorotation principle still applies, as the air flowing up and through the rotor maintains the rotor speed. A lifting force is therefore produced which, although insufficient to maintain the machine's altitude, prevents it from falling like a stone. Even when the propeller is stopped, the autogiro will descend safely, gliding with forward speed to a normal landing.

In this respect, the autogiro is at some advantage over the helicopter, since in the case of helicopter engine failure the climbing pitch angle of the rotors (about 11°) would quickly stop them, with disastrous results. To keep his rotors turning the pilot will have to quickly reduce the pitch angle of his blades to that which provides autorotation for a safe forced landing.

Overcoming instability

The first successful autogiro was designed by Juan de la Cierva and was flown on 9 January 1923, at Getafe Airdrome near Madrid. This was his fourth design; the other three had suffered from an alarming tendency to roll over when moving forward.

The instability was due to the use of rigid rotor blades. With the machine moving forward and the rotor turning, the blade turning into the airstream undergoes a greater lifting force than the opposite blade which is moving downstream. With rigid rotor blades, this imbalance is transmitted to the whole machine, producing, a rolling motion. To overcome this instability, Cierva designed a rotor system with blades suitably hinged at the root, so

Below: Juan de la Cierva by one of his first autogiros in 1925. The wings are ailerons, necessary because the rotor was not fully controllable.

that rather than transmit the imbalance to the whole machine, it was taken up by the individual blades which could move accordingly.

At the root of each blade he fitted two hinges. One, the *flapping hinge*, allowed the blade to flap up and down; the other, the *drag hinge*, permitted the necessary sideways movement.

The autogiro rotor blade (or that of the helicopter) is not, by itself, stiff enough to carry the weight of the machine. It is the enormous CENTRIFUGAL FORCE of rotation that keeps the rotors moving in an almost flat path, and even though they have flapping hinges at their roots, the weight of the machine is carried here.

Modifications

The autogiro was the forerunner of the helicopter and did much to help its development. The late 1920s and the following decade saw the autogiro's heyday, with many improvements and modifications which were to become permanent features of the then new vertical take off and landing machines called helicopters. After a period of stagnation, however, there are signs of a revival of the autogiro. Its relative simplicity of construction and maintenance, combined with stable and efficient operation, are useful for surveying and reconnaissance.

See also: Aerial photography; Aerodynamics; Aero engine; Aircraft; Airplane; Aviation; Centrifuge; Helicopter; Propeller, aircraft.

Automatic weapon

When describing small arms mechanisms, the term automatic is usually applied to a system in which the full cycle of operations is carried out as soon as the trigger is pressed; while the trigger remains pressed, the cycle is repeated continuously. This means that the weapon fires, extracts the empty case, ejects it from the pistol, compresses the return spring, feeds a round from the magazine and places it in the chamber ready for firing. The hammer, or firing pin, then strikes the cap of the cartridge and another round is fired.

A great number of automatic weapons are, in fact, selfloading or semiautomatic because the trigger mechanism is so designed that the trigger must be released and subsequently operated again to fire another round.

There are basically two methods of designing a gun to fire automatically. It can either be motor fed and motor driven – usually by electric motor – or it can employ the Maxim principle which uses the recoil to perform the complete cycle of operations.

When a bullet is fired the pressure of released gases which drive it down the barrel is as great backward as forward. The American, Hiram Stevens Maxim, was the first man to use this force to push the bolt back, eject the empty bullet case and pull a new round into position. The new round is then pushed into the barrel by the returning, spring-loaded bolt, locked and fired.

Maxim's invention was the fully automatic machine gun and it was belt fed – which is still popular today. However in light machine guns and in semiautomatic weapons it is more usual to have a spring-loaded magazine to push the next round up into position ready for the returning breech mechanism to push it into the barrel.

This principle of producing automatic fire by using the recoil caused by gas pressure is common to virtually all infantry small arms and personal weapons in modern forces. The most powerful of these is the general-purpose machine gun (GPMG) which can perform all the necessary tasks. Fairly

Below: Members of the British Gurkha battalion in the Falklands with 7.62 mm LIAI self-loading rifles.

Above: The Israeli 9 mm Uzi submachine gun is deadly, yet light and easy to handle.

RSAF INDIVIDUAL WEAPON SYSTEM

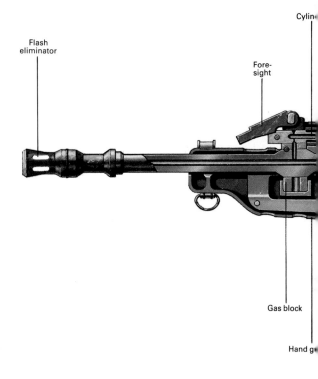

Flash eliminator

Fore-sight

Cylin

Gas block

Hand g

Above: The British Army's 5.56 mm Individual Weapon is part of the SA-80 small arms family, developed from the Royal Small Arms Factory's experimental 4.85 mm assault rifle.

typical of a GPMG is the U.S. Army's M60. Although it performs all its tasks adequately it is not entirely satisfactory in any of them. As a light machine gun, which is what an infantry section requires, it suffers from the handicap of weighing more than 30 lb (14 kg) unloaded. That is a lot for an infantryman to carry. An additional disadvantage is the trailing edges of the belt, which can become caught in undergrowth and hedges as the gunner doubles to a new firing position. If this happens, the entire belt feed can become jammed, leaving the weapon inoperable. In spite of all this it is difficult to see what sort of weapon can provide a replacement for the GPMG.

The most outstandingly successful rifle since World War II has been the Soviet AK-47 which was designed by Mikhail Kalashnikov and fires 7.62 mm ammunition with acceptable accuracy. It uses the gas pressure produced when a bullet is fired. In the AK-47, and most other types of automatic rifles, the backward pressure is used to push the bolt back, eject the empty bullet case and allow a new round into position. This can then be pushed into the barrel by the returning spring-loaded bolt and fired.

The AK-47 is fed by a 30-round, detachable magazine and can be used to fire single shots as well as bursts of fire.

The AK-47 has not been without rivals. The most significant of these is the Armalite, which was designed some 20 years ago by Eugene Stoner. One of the chief difficulties in equipping an infantryman is to keep down the weight he has to carry in action. The Armalite AR-15 solved some of the problems by being designed to fire a lightweight bullet at such high velocity that it was as lethal and accurate as heavier rounds. Lightweight materials such as nylon, plastic and metal alloys were used in manufacturing the AR-15 and it overcame initial teething problems to prove itself reliable. New rifles with smaller, lighter rounds are now entering service.

Submachine guns

The rifle is the most typical and useful personal weapon of an infantryman, but for special situations he may use a *pistol* or *submachine gun*. These are both comparatively inaccurate weapons, firing low velocity rounds, and used for close range work.

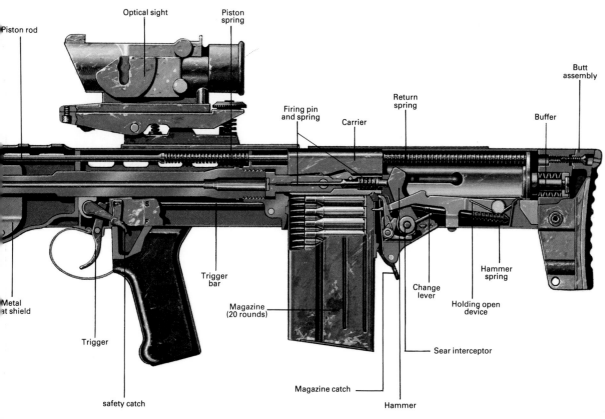

Labels (clockwise from top left): Piston rod, Optical sight, Piston spring, Firing pin and spring, Carrier, Return spring, Butt assembly, Buffer, Hammer spring, Holding open device, Change lever, Sear interceptor, Hammer, Magazine catch, Magazine (20 rounds), Trigger bar, Metal at shield, Trigger, safety catch

Behind their personal weapons is a long line of increasingly heavier weaponry to support infantry in battle. The smallest unit of riflemen is normally a section, which contains about ten men and would usually be equipped with a *machine gun* and a one-man *antitank weapon*.

Automatic pistol

The truly automatic pistol is rare but amongst the few that are found are the Russian Stechkin and the Czechoslovakian Vzor 61 (Skorpian); both of these can be set to produce either self loading or fully automatic fire. The reason for the unpopularity of the fully automatic pistol is its lack of accuracy. The light weight of the recoiling parts and the lightness of the return spring produce a high rate of fire. On firing, the pistol kicks upwards above the line of the firer's hand gripping the butt, which causes the muzzle to rise at a successively increasing rate as each round is discharged. After a short burst of firing at 750 rounds a minute, which is typical of the fully automatic pistol, the muzzle could be pointing upwards at 60°. With self loading pistols the aim can be corrected between shots and a greater chance of a hit can be expected.

Operation of the automatic pistol

Pistols of small caliber, up to .32, are almost invari-ably of blowback design, operating with an unlocked breech block.

Above this caliber locked breech designs are used. Nearly all types employ the recoil method of opera-tion, where the breech block is locked to the barrel. On firing they move back together until the gas pressure is at a safe level, when the barrel stops and the breech block continues to the rear.

To prepare for firing the slide is fully pulled back, allowing a round to be placed in the chamber. It then moves forward, and the barrel is locked on to the slide by ribs on the top slotting into recesses in the slide. When the trigger is pulled the hammer is released and drives the firing pin forward through the breech face. The bullet moves down the bore and the gas pressure against the cartridge case pushes it back hard against the breech face, which forms part of the slide. The slide goes back but is connected to the barrel, which recoils with it.

The underside of the barrel has a link connected to the nonrecoiling frame. As the barrel goes back the link rotates and drags the rear end of the barrel down. The ribs on the barrel come out of engage-ment with the slide and the slide continues to recoil on its own; it extracts and ejects the empty case, feeds in a new round and springs forward to recon-nect with the barrel. It carries the barrel foward and the weapon is ready to fire again. The trigger mechanism includes a disconnector which ensures that to release the hammer the trigger must first be released and then pressed again.

This type of pistol is simple, reliable, and robust. Because the barrel moves up and down, the front bearing must have a large clearance and this leads to wear as the gun ages.

Features of the automatic pistol

The automatic pistol has frequently been compared with the revolver, and both have advantages and disadvantages. The advantages of the automatic may be summarized as: larger ammunition capacity than the revolver; quicker reloading, provided a loaded magazine is available; higher muzzle VELOC-ITY – no gas leak; and lightness and compactness.

Its disadvantages are: unreliability under adverse conditions, such as areas that cause mud or sand to enter the mechanism; a closed mechanism which makes inspection difficult and detracts from safety; a need for more frequent maintenance; and its mechanical complexity.

The revolver is also a type of automatic weapon but one which uses the manual pressure of its user upon the trigger or the hammer to manage the cycle of bringing a new round into the firing position rather than gas pressure. This principle was used in the machine gun's immediate ancestor, the Gatling gun, in which the operator cranked the mechanism. More sophisticated Gatlings have made a comeback in recent times and the U.S. Vulcan Phalanx, which is motor driven as one electric motor rotates its barrels and another feeds in ammunition, has become justly famous for its extremely high rate of fire of 6000 rounds a minute.

The idea of using a motor to produce automatic firing is not confined to multibarreled weapons. The Hughes Chain Gun family used by the U.S. Army in 30 mm, 25 mm and .762 mm versions has a single barrel and a rotating bolt mechanism that is powered by a reliable chain drive. This chain mechanismed action is something of a Hughes speciality but the use of other types of motor drive in automatic weapons is becoming more and more popular – particularly with very heavy machine guns and cannon. These weapons are designed to be carried in helicopters or armored fighting vehicles so the extra weight of an incorporated motor is not the problem it would be to a dismounted infantryman, and the system has the virtue of greater reliability than gas recoil systems. Typical of these is the GUA-8/A-30 Gatling which can fire 2000 to 4000 30 mm shells per minute up to 1.8 miles (3 km).

See also: Ammunition; Ballistics; Bullet; Dynamics; Gun; Revolver; Rifle; Machine gun.

Above: The Soviet AK-47 automatic rifle has proved successful among regular as well as guerrilla armies; these are captured pieces.

Below: An early Gatling mechanism – essentially a continuous series of gun barrels – which relied on the operator's crank to fire and reload.

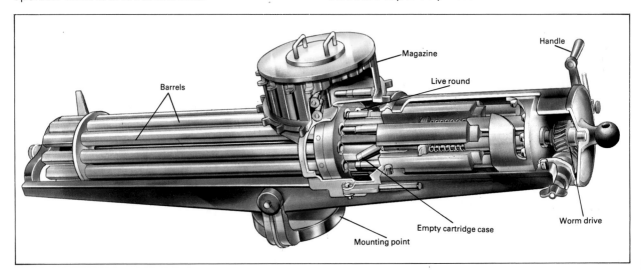

Barrels

Magazine

Handle

Live round

Worm drive

Empty cartridge case

Mounting point

Automobile

Ever since the late 1700s various inventors had worked at the idea of a self-propelled carriage. For nearly a hundred years, the only way in which this might be achieved was through the use of a steam engine. However, after the publication of Otto's paper on the four-stroke cycle in 1870, it became clear that the internal-combustion engine was likely to be a better bet for a road-going vehicle.

In the following ten years several inventors built themselves "one of a kind" vehicles powered by such engines and it was only a matter of time before somebody began to build his design in series and offer it for commercial sale. The vital move took place in Germany in the mid-1880s when both Benz and Daimler began to build their first automobiles. The Benz was a lightweight three wheeler which owed much to the then-popular technology of the bicycle; the Daimler was a heavier four-wheeler which borrowed most of its construction details from the horse-drawn carriage.

If Germany was the country in which the automobile first took commercial shape, France was certainly the place where it received much of its early technical development, and during the 1890s many of the names still familiar today, including Peugeot and Renault, began to turn the automobile from a primitive vehicle which depended on horse-drawn technology, into a machine much more logically laid out and better suited to the needs of its driver and passengers. In particular, by 1898 the rival companies of Panhard-Levassor and Renault had between them arrived at the mechanical layout which remained almost constant for the next sixty years, with the engine installed at the front, the transmission immediately behind it, and the drive taken through a jointed drive shaft to the back axle and thus to the rear wheels.

The center of automobile activity then moved in large measure to the U.S., where the efforts of the automobile pioneers of the 1890s quickly turned to industrial success in the 1900s. Several of those pioneers thought in much larger-scale industrial terms than any of their European counterparts, and it only needed the vision of Henry Ford to link the automobile to the latest kind of production technology (in the form of the continuous-chain assembly line) to turn it from a rich man's toy into an essential tool and means of transport for thousands of people. The first Model T came off the line in Detroit in October 1908, barely twenty years after the first trickle of Benz and Daimler cars had emerged from their German workshops. The U.S. established itself almost overnight as the world's greatest producer of automobiles and remained firmly in that position until the late 1970s.

Above: The automobile has gained a special place in society, so town and city planners must allow for its use and storage, while minimizing its polluting impact on the environment.

After World War I, automobile development advanced along two parallel paths. In the U.S. that path was one of smooth and continual improvement. Many authorities accuse the American automobile engineer of lacking the vision and adventure of his European rivals, but the fact remains that many of the inventions which turned the automobile into a truly practical proposition, easy to drive and efficient in operation, came from the U.S. the electric starter motor as early as 1912, coil-and-distributor ignition from the General Motors research laboratories of the 1920s, effective synchromesh for gearboxes, low-pressure tires, and eventually the first workable automatic transmission and power-assisted steering.

While the Americans were steadily advancing, the Europeans were casting around for some way of making the automobile more widely available in markets where economic conditions were much more depressed. This led the most imaginative of European engineers, like Lancia in Italy and Citroen in France, to seek ways of making the automobile lighter and more economical. Lancia was the first to point out the benefits of unitary body construction, while Citroen pioneered front-wheel drive. Also, the intense competition of European motor sport – fed by national rivalry of a kind which could not exist in the U.S. – led to other notable technical advances such as independent suspension, four-wheel brakes and much more efficient engines. By the outbreak of the World War II, the automobile was a little more than half-way through its process of development from the earliest Benz to the present day, but already the American car was larger, better equipped and in real terms cheaper than its European equivalent. The best European models, however, boasted a fuel economy which no American car could match.

There are three main areas of automobile engineering research today. One concerns the further development of the main mechanical units – the engine, transmission and tires in particular – in search of fundamentally better efficiency and safety. The second is the application of new materials, especially plastic composites for the body and ceramics for the engine. The third and easily the most immediately promising is the use of electronic systems to achieve anything from better engine efficiency to automatic fault detection.

Above: The use of glass-reinforced plastic to make strong, lightweight bodywork is not a new idea. This 1953 Chevrolet Corvette has a plastic body, giving excellent power-to-weight ratio.

The body

Automobile bodies started out either as copies of horse-drawn carriages, or as simple platforms upon which the seats were mounted. By 1900 however a virtually standard layout had already been arrived at, with a chassis frame composed of two lengthwise members joined by crossbeams. The superstructure mounted on this chassis served no purpose other than to keep out some of the wind and rain, and of course to make the vehicle look better. By the mid-1920s some engineers were already looking at ways of making the body shell self-supporting, so as to save the weight of the chassis frame. Lancia in Europe and Budd in the U.S. pioneered this thinking, and the Budd system of pressed-steel panels welded together to form a torsion box was eventually widely adopted, especially in Europe where Citroen was quick to adopt the idea. In the U.S., the bodies of larger automobiles still sometimes use a hybrid construction, with the welded steel shell partly supported by a *perimeter frame*. Another modern technique is to mount the main mechanical components on subframes which are then bolted to the body. Subframes ease problems of assembly and assist insulation of the passenger cabin against road noise.

The modern body engineer has four main aims. He must make the body as light as possible for the sake of economy, and this means using computers to

Left: A prototype Aston Martin Bulldog sports car undergoing aerodynamic tests in a wind tunnel. With a top speed of 190 mph (305 km/hr), the body will be streamlined not only to reduce drag and so give good fuel consumption, but to make the car stable. Below: This three cylinder diesel by Volkswagen has a capacity of only 1191 cc, but develops 45 bhp (33 kw) and is up to 15 per cent more economical than other compact cars of its type and class.

work out stresses, and high-strength steel and other new materials to save endless bulk. He must adopt a smooth body shape which gives the least possible aerodynamic drag, again for the sake of economy, while also bearing in mind the need for good natural stability. He must ensure that the body meets current legislation for safety, and finally he must provide sufficient protection against corrosion. This last requirement has become severe since automobile manufacturers began offering six-year warranties against body rusting, and has been responsible for the strong current interest in plastics for use in vulnerable areas of the body.

The engine

The engine designer has always faced a multitude of problems of which the most basic are the way in which fuel is mixed with air and delivered to the engine, the way the valves are operated, the manner in which the ignition spark is generated, and the way the engine is lubricated and cooled. The earliest engines had but one cylinder but it was quickly realized that multiple cylinders permitted better balancing and hence smoother running. Four cylinders became the norm for smaller cars, with six or eight cylinders for larger models. Six cylinders may be in-line or in a more compact V layout – two banks of three, usually with a 60° angle between them. Eight cylinder engines are nearly always in V-8, with a 90° angle between the banks.

The carburetor is the traditonal way of delivering fuel and mixing it with air in the right proportion. Early carburetors were very simple but limited in the amount of fuel they could deliver. Modern units often have multiple barrels – in other words, more than one inlet to the engine – and have become complicated by devices which apply corrections to give

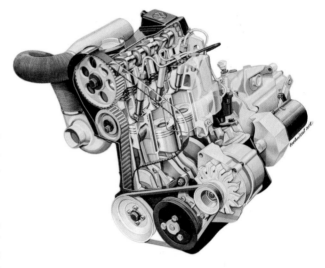

smooth running and low exhaust emissions in all circumstances. Today the carburetor is being increasingly challenged by fuel injection in which fuel is squirted from a high-pressure gallery either into the main engine intake or directly into the inlet passage to each cylinder. Most modern injection systems depend on electronic control systems to work out the correct amount of fuel to inject for each engine operating condition. These electronic systems often also control the generation and timing of the ignition spark, since there is an obvious economy in using the same computer for both tasks. Even where carburetors are still used, electronic ignition systems have become near-standard in modern automobiles especially in those countries where exhaust emission regulations are severe. An increasing number of modern engines use turbocharging to increase the air supply and thus the maximum power available; some automobiles are powered by the diesel engine which has no ignition system but depends on the heat due to very high compression to cause combustion.

The inlet and exhaust valves are operated by one or more camshafts driven at half crankshaft speed. At one time, almost all camshafts were chain-driven (except for a few high-performance cars which used gear drive) but today many engines use toothed rubber belts which need no lubrication.

Transmission

The automobile transmission carries out three tasks. It enables the engine to run when the vehicle is not moving; it multiplies the engine driving force or torque and enables the engine to run at an efficient speed whatever the speed of the car; and it carries the drive to the wheels. The traditional form of transmission is through a manually operated clutch and multispeed gears, and a drive shaft to the rear wheels. However, the majority of modern American automobiles use some form of automatic transmission with a hydraulic torque converter and epicyclic gear train in place of the manual clutch and layshaft gears. Today there is much interest in the belt-and-pulley driven *continuously variable transmission* (CVT) especially for small European automobiles. These small models today have their engines installed across the car, with the transmission configured to drive the front wheels. Another area of interest for the transmission designer is that of driving all four wheels instead of just two – a technique no longer confined to off-road and leisure vehicles. There is also a growing interest in *limited-slip differentials* which modify the traditional differential gear (whose purpose is to allow the driven wheels to travel at different speeds when rounding a curve) so that some drive force is transmitted even when one wheel slips.

Suspension

For many years, automobile suspensions consisted simply of multiple-leaf springs upon which the axles were mounted. Such suspensions offered poor comfort if they were stiff enough to locate the axles properly, and suffered from *tramp* (driven-wheel

Several factors have influenced car design during the last three decades, and the effects of all these factors can be seen by comparing the stages in development of any model. The designers of the 1953 Buick Skylark (top) aimed for grand flowing curves without regard to the complexities of metal forming techniques. The 5276 cc V-8 engine developed 188 bhp (140 kw) and had fuel consumption of 12.8 mpg. The 1971 Buick Electra (middle) had improved visibility and simpler body sections; its 7456 cc V-8 developed 315 bhp (235 kw) and returned 11.4 mpg. The 1982 Buick Century (bottom) sports a slim bumper designed, like the extremities of the car, to crumple and absorb shock on impact. Its 2966 cc V-6 developed 110 bhp (82 kw), but at only half the weight of the other two models and with a streamlined body, it returned a generous 22.5 mpg as well as a sporty performance.

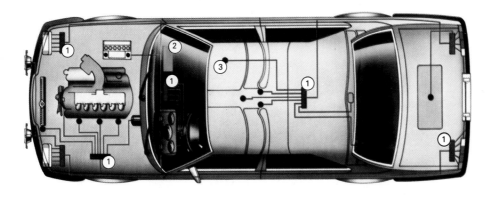

Left: In a typical computer-controlled automobile, sensors (3) monitor factors such as oil pressure, engine temperature, and fuel flow. The readings are digitized in substations (1) and sent to a central controller (2) which sends back coded signals to the various subscriber stations which respond.

bounce) and poor stability if the springs were soft enough to give a comfortable ride. Eventually *independent suspension* was adopted, in which the wheels were not joined by an axle beam but could move independently. Today, all automobiles except a few off-roaders have independent front suspension, and a growing number use independent rear suspension also. Nearly all independent suspension systems use coil-type springs together with telescopic hydraulic *dampers* whose purpose is to stop the springs from oscillating out of control. There are various ways of locating each wheel so that it remains upright relative to the vehicle body. Double wishbones remain popular, but the MacPherson strut layout is ever more frequently used; semitrailing arms are a cost-effective option for independent rear suspension. A few very advanced automobiles, notably those of Citroen, use a high-pressure hydropneumatic suspension system which gives automatic body levelling and adjustable ride height. It seems likely that electronic control systems will soon be used to give *active ride control* which could lead to much improved comfort.

Steering, brakes and tires

Where steering, brakes and tires are concerned, the last ten years have seen steady moves in three particular areas. Most automobiles, certainly in Europe and increasingly also in Japan and the US, now use *rack and pinion* steering which has proved to offer the most precise control. The majority of American automobiles use power-assisted steering, using hydraulic pressure from an engine-driven pump, and this feature is also seen in more and more European and Japanese cars. Disc-type front brakes are now almost universal, giving greater resistance to brake *fade*, but the more traditional drum-type brake is still more often used at the rear, not least because it makes the design of the parking brake much easier. Another near-universal feature is the brake-assistance *servo* which uses the suction effect from a reservoir connected to the engine inlet manifold. One of the latest brake system developments is *antilock braking* which depends on the electronic detection of wheel-slowing to cause a momentary release of the brake. Improved braking performance goes hand in hand with the improved stability and grip of radial-ply tires which have almost completely replaced the traditional cross-ply type. There is an increasing tendency for modern tires to become lower in relation to their width, with an *aspect ratio* of 70 per cent now commonplace.

Electrical systems

Finally, no modern automobile would be complete without extensive electrical systems which today call for a good deal of power. The AC alternator, with built-in transistor rectifier, replaced the less efficient DC generator about 20 years ago; today, the electrical system designer is seeking ways to reduce the sheer bulk of wiring and accessories. One of the most likely solutions is to use MULTIPLEXING which enables a single wire to be used for several control tasks on a time-sharing basis, thanks to the use of electronic microprocessors.

See also: Battery; Brake; Diesel engine; Ignition system, car; Internal combustion engine.

• FACT FILE •

- The world's first automobile was probably a steam-powered truck which the French Ministry of War tested in 1770 as a potential cannon carrier. The prototype carried 4 passengers at 2½ mph (4 km/h), and had to stop every 15 minutes for a boiler refill.

- Between 1961 and 1968 3000 German Amphicars were produced. The amphibious vehicle was powered by a Triumph engine, and could reach 68 mph (110 km/h) on land and 6½ knots (12 km/h) in the water.

Plastic car from Italy

The "car of the future" is by now a fairly familiar sight; it keeps cropping up at motor shows and in movies, invariably sleek-looking and equally invariably wholly impracticable. But Fiat has recently shown a car that gives some very clear indications of the way that the small car is likely to go, not just because it employs new materials – principally new plastics – which make it lighter and therefore more fuel efficient than a conventional steel equivalent, but because the plastic bodyshell will be moldable into far more aerodynamic shapes, it will not corrode, will not need painting and will provide a far stronger and safer passenger cell. But the prototype's greatest possibilities lie in the fact that it will need less energy to produce and – unlike most other future car concepts – is technologically and industrially feasible.

The VSS (Vettura Sperimentale a Sottisisstemi – Experimental Subsystem Car) started life as a research project but is currently a fully-operational prototype which shows a totally new approach to car design philosophy.

Fiat's objectives were to explore new production techniques, find ways of reducing overall weight and to find a basic skeleton which, once built and in production, would not need to be changed or even adapted when the bodyshell is periodically restyled. What this also means is that the same skeleton is used for all models in the range – sedan, sports car, GT, or station wagon.

This has been achieved by separating the load-bearing function and the need to provide passenger protection from the body shell, whereas current designs use the entire welded body to provide the necessary torsional rigidity, strength and passenger protection.

The basic framework is constructed from zinc-treated box-section and sheet steel, computer-designed to ensure that the necessary stresses can be accommodated by the lightest possible structure. Thus the center section forms a protective cage for the driver and passengers, while the front and rear sections in addition to carrying the engine and front suspension, and rear suspension assembly respectively, absorb impact energy in the event of an accident.

What makes this whole concept so attractive is that once you have this basic skeleton, virtually any shape or design of body can be bolted on top. And the use of plastics becomes the icing on the cake because it gives the stylist far more freedom than sheet steel would ever allow.

The plastics themselves have been produced by the U.S. General Electric Plastics Company at their Dutch subsidiary. Being self-colored, they will not need painting and will not scratch or chip as painted metal does. Because the material is elastic to a degree, minor dents will pop straight out again and even in the case of more serious impacts, damage will be more confined – an impact on one of the rear fenders will not cause ripples down the length of the car. Totally fire-resistant, the bodyshells should last a minimum of twenty years compared to the steel car's average of around half that time.

Above: Four different versions of Fiat's prototype VSS plastic car could be built on the same chassis and on the same assembly line.

On the car itself, the principle of function separation – mentioned above – is continued into each of the ten subsystems of the VSS. Therefore, different plastics are used on different parts of the car; more elastic at the front and rear of the car where a degree of flexibility is needed to cope with minor impacts, more rigid in other areas.

The various body subsystems are easily apparent in cutaway drawings. The front end consists of the bumper which is rigidly fastened to the basic steel structure by means of brackets, and the frontal section which incorporates the radiator grill, air intake and headlights.

The roof, doors and rear hatch are of fairly conventional structure and shape, but the clear advantages of plastics over steel are most obvious in the hood and trunk.

Traditionally, steel would be used to make the four separate elements that enclose the engine compartment: the hood itself; the inner framework; and the two front fender assemblies. But on the VSS, this is a single molded unit extended as far as the wheel arches. Quite apart from the fact that this is simpler to manufacture and fit than four separate steel units, an indication of the weight-saving possibilities of VSS-type construction is that the average small-to-medium-size car hood weighs around 37 lbs (17 kg) in steel, while the complete VSS assembly in plastic – polyester resin reinforced with glass fiber in this case – weighs just 26 lbs (12 kg). And that sort of weight-saving applies to every body component.

This bonding together of separate parts – which can quite easily be done off the main production lines – followed by one simple bolting operating, is the key to what is probably the most significant element of the whole VSS exercise.

The main loadbearing steel structure would be built and welded on-line; but once the manufacturer has invested in the basic tooling needed to build the frame (the pressing and welding tools and templates), no further costs would be incurred, even in the event of a major restyling exercise, because the framework could and would remain unchanged, saving manufacturers and customers hundreds of millions of dollars.

Just when a car such as the Fiat VSS will go into production depends mostly upon economic considerations – despite the overall energy saving in using plastics. Although derived from oil, the various plastics used in the VSS are made from oil processing by-products which have few other applications; and the energy required to process the plastic materials is around half the equivalent steel alternative. But the cost of these specialized plastics is still too great for any manufacturer to go into production.

There can be little doubt, however, that within a decade a VSS-type car will be a viable proposition. For this prototype, Fiat used existing Fiat Ritmo engine, transmission and suspension components; not only is the overall weight of the VSS over 20 per cent less than the Strada but it is estimated that the total production cycle of the VSS would be five hours less than that of the Ritmo.

Aviation

The science of designing, building and flying air-craft has its origins in the work of the Montgolfier brothers in France during the eighteenth century, who made balloons from silk and linen bags placed over a fire. The French scientist Pilâtre de Rozier was the first man to be lifted in a balloon, a Mont-golfier model, in October 1783. One month later the King of France's cousin became the first passenger, on a flight over Paris. In 1797 the French balloonist Garnerin made the first successful human descent by parachute, again from a balloon.

But, it was the development of the heavier-than-air craft that lead to the science of aviation as we today define it. Much of the theoretical work had been done in the nineteenth century. The essential problem was to generate enough mechanical force to allow forward speed to increase the lift above a wing until the upward force became greater than the downward pull of gravity.

In 1809 Sir George Cayley had outlined the forces of thrust, drag and lift, and had pointed out the value of the cambered, or arched airfoil wing shape in preference to the flat plate. Cayley had flown model gliders as early as 1804 and had flown at least two full-sized gliders before his death in 1857. Otto Lilienthal carried on the glider work, making more than 2000 successful flights between 1891 and 1896, exercising control by shifting his weight beneath the flying wing. At the time of his death in 1896 he was working on a body harness attached to a rear elevator.

To provide the necessary forward thrust, designers first tried steam engines. The biggest of them was made by W. S. Henson in 1842 for the Aerial Steam Carriage. It had a tail-piece to provide control and stability, box-kite wings and a three-wheeled undercarriage. It was to have a span of 150 ft (46 m) with wings incorporating spars and ribs and to be propelled by two six-blade airscrews. It was, how-ever, never built.

In 1894 Hiram Maxim staged an elaborate experiment to prove the existence of the phenomenon of lift with a device that weighed 3.5 tons and applied 360 hp through two steam engines. It lifted momentarily from its rails, and there the project ended. In France people like du Temple de la Croix, Penaud and Ader worked on various models driven by steam, twisted rubber and clockwork.

With the development of the gasoline engine, however, the mathematics of powered flight became a reality. In October 1903 Samuel P. Langley, Secretary to the Smithsonian Institute in Washington, came close with a gas-powered aircraft launched by catapult from a houseboat on the Potomac River. Two months later, the Wright brothers succeeded in achieving powered flight.

Below: The Boeing 747 Jumbo Jet is powered by four Pratt and Whitney JT9D turbofan engines.

Above: Wilbur Wright, having just let go of the wing, watches brother Orville at the controls of The Flyer as it takes off from a wooden rail in December 1903 and flies away from the camera.
Right: An eighteenth century hot air balloon fueled by the burning of chopped straw.

The Wright brothers

Orville and Wilbur Wright had searched for an automobile engine which was light enough to be mounted on the fragile structure of their glider, but powerful enough to give them lift. None could be found, so they built their own; a four-cylinder motor, weighing 15 lbs (7 kg) and producing 12 hp. It turned two wooden propellers behind the wings, while the pilot lay on his stomach with a wire string attached to his waist, twisting the wingtips and balancing the aircraft in flight. On December 17, 1903 Orville Wright piloted The Flyer 120 ft (37 m) in a flight lasting 12 seconds. Three more flights were made that day and the last succeeded in covering a magnificent 852 ft (260 m).

At first the Wright's achievement caused little stir. It was only with their third airplane that interest was generated. In 1905 it managed a flight of 24 miles (38 km) at an average speed of 38 mph (61 kmph); its success owed much to the Wrights' experiments in control.

In 1908 Wilbur Wright demonstrated the latest model in France, where he made several long flights, including one of 2 hours, 20 minutes on 31 December. It gave a great impetus to European designers, who had previously concentrated on stability, rather than control.

In 1909 an Englishman, A. V. Roe, produced a tractor biplane and a fellow countryman, J. W. Dunne, built the world's first swept-wing airplane, again a biplane, aimed at inherent stability. A year later F. W. Lancaster put forward his theory of the circulation of air over wing surfaces, a theory which has since been proved to be true.

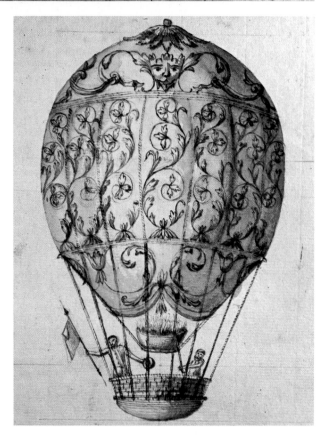

At the Rheims aviation week in August 1909 more than 30 aircraft were on show, six built to the Wright's specification. But their influence on European design did not last long. After the first successful crossing of the English Channel by Louis Bleriot in the same year, in a monoplane, European builders started going their own way. The best performers were still biplanes, but a good deal of work went into monoplane designs and the idea of the cantilever wing, supported by the fuselage instead of wires, was contained in a patent registered by Junkers of Germany in 1910. A year later another improve-

Above: The U.S. F86F-30 Sabre was a transonic craft, being capable of exceeding Mach 1 only in a dive. It employed the German innovation of swept back wings to reduce drag but it needed an even more streamlined shape in the guise of the F-100 Super Sabre of 1953 to break the sound barrier in level flight. Left: The A300 Airbus was one of the first planes to use super-critical wings and composites.

ment appeared in a German device for raising the undercarriage legs on hinges to lie flush with the fuselage in flight.

By 1913 a host of important achievements and events had been recorded. The air speed record stood at 126.6 mph (204 kmph), the French pilot Adolphe Pégoud had looped the loop for the first time and the Schneider Trophy Race for seaplanes had been inaugurated. Then World War I broke out.

World War I

The flimsy, boxlike structures with underpowered engines of 1914 were soon replaced as designers took up the task of building combat aircraft. The most significant developments, however, were not structural. Aircraft became sturdier, it is true, their engines more efficient and designs such as Fokker's high-wing monoplane, with a fuselage suspended beneath with built-in, stressed-skin construction, would lead to major advances in later years. But the most important advance came in the way aircraft were designed for specialized operations.

In the early years aircraft were used as army scouts; by 1918 the British Handley Page V/1500

four-engined biplane could carry 1000 lb (450 kg) of bombs over Berlin, and German Gothas could dump similar loads over London. Fighters could fly at 140 to 150 mph (220 to 240 kph) and climb to an altitude of 23,000 ft (7000 m).

When peace came there was a large fleet of ex-military aircraft available to passenger and mail transport operators. The large, wire-braced biplanes of the war years scored some significant success immediately after 1918. The Atlantic was crossed in May 1919, by an American flying boat – though it stopped several times and took two weeks. A month later a Vickers Vimy, piloted by John Alcock and Arthur Whitten-Brown flew non-stop from Newfoundland to Ireland; but the wood, fabric and wire designs were on the way out, hastened by aircraft designed for endurance and high-speed record attempts, the use of air-cooled, rather than the heavier water-cooled engine and the growing needs of the passenger transport industry.

During this period, work started on helicopters, pioneered in the U.S. by Sikorsky and in Germany by Focke and Achgelis. At the same time the Spaniard, Juan de la Cierva, invented the autogiro; an aircraft

which has an unpowered rotor turned by the backwash from an ordinary airscrew.

In 1927 Charles Lindbergh's Ryan monoplane, The Spirit of St Louis flew 3600 miles non-stop in 33 hours, 39 minutes, from New York to Paris; and in 1928 Charles Kingsford-Smith crossed the Pacific in a three-engined Fokker monoplane Southern Cross.

These were more than just feats of personal endurance, they underlined the growing reliability of aircraft and designs started incorporating navigational and radio equipment to further enhance safety in the air.

Hinged flaps were added to the rear of wings to increase lift and resistance at low speed. This allowed planes to land more slowly and use shorter airfields. Then a new range of passenger aircraft emerged; aircraft such as the Boeing 247 of 1933 and the Douglas DC range of 1934.

They were reasonably large, featured soundproofing, and offered passengers a degree of unprecedented comfort. For sea crossings, large flying boats were built by Latécoère of France, Glenn Martin and Boeing in the U.S.

During the 1930s designers also began experimenting with the jet engine. The first jet aircraft flight was in August 1939, by the German Heinkel He 178. This development was accelerated by World War II, which started the same year. In May 1941 the first British jet, the Whittle engined Gloster, made its maiden flight. The U.S. followed in 1942 with the Bell XP 59A. Supersonic flight was achieved in 1947 with the U.S. Bell X-1. Immediately

Above: A Bell AH-IG Huey Cobra gunship in the Mekong Delta, Vietnam, in 1967. It has a Lycoming turboshaft engine and a range of 230 miles (370 km).

after the war the U.S. concentrated on developing piston-engined, propeller-driven airliners like the Douglas DC 7 and the Lockheed Starliner, carrying 100 passengers at over 300 mph (480 kph); the British concentrated on jet engines, introducing a Rolls Royce turboprop Dart engine to the De Havilland Viscount range in 1948. In 1952 the all-jet Comet appeared, but the original square cabin windows failed in the early models, leading to a series of crashes. By the time the revised Comet 4 appeared in 1958 the Boeing 707 had emerged and the U.S. dominated the civil air transport industry.

The latest range of commercial airliners – such as the Airbus A310 – is starting to incorporate *fly-by-wire* electronics, connecting the cockpit to the flaps and airfoils by electronics, rather than mechanical links. The use of electronics means that future airliners are being designed to be inherently unstable. This cuts down the cost of materials which presently have to ensure that an aircraft will return to the horizontal once it is tipped out of position; a computer works out the controls in order to maintain stability. And turbo-prop engines are returning to favor as new materials and technology have solved the problem of drag created by propellers revolving at the speed of sound.

See also: Aerospace industry; Aircraft; Airplane; Airships; Balloon; Helicopter.

Avionics

An aircraft's avionics are the electronic systems which provide the pilot with navigational and other data and help him to control the plane.

The word avionics comes from AVIation electrONICS, the technology of electronics used in aircraft communications, navigation and flight management. In military aircraft it also covers electronically controlled weapons, reconnaissance and detection systems.

Communications

Short distance air to ground communication is usually on VHF (very high frequency) channels in the aviation frequency band 118 to 135.975 MHz. The power transmitted by airborne equipment is usually up to 25 watts. The signals travel only in the line of sight, so the range depends on the aircraft's altitude. With aircraft flying at 27,000 ft (8230 m), ranges of 250 miles (400 km) are normal. Military aircraft also use UHF (ultra high frequency) channels in the 225 to 399.95 MHz band with similar air to ground range and up to 600 miles (965 km) air range. Worldwide communication is allocated to aircraft in certain channels in the band of 2 to 30 MHz. Powers of up to 400 W are used with a choice of telemetry methods, such as voice and telegraph. Low frequency (60 to 160 kHz) radio teleprinter equipment is sometimes fitted on large commercial aircraft.

A selective calling system is used so that the flight crew does not have to listen constantly to the radio system for incoming calls. In the SELCAL mode, the calling station sends out a two-tone signal, coded for the particular aircraft being called. The airborne receiver is left tuned to the calling frequency, and can be heard all the time. When the aircraft code is received and decoded, the flight crew is alerted by a visual or audible signal, and only then need give its attention to the radio.

Automatic pilot

The automatic pilot was demonstrated as early as 1914 when Lawrence Sperry, son of Dr Elmer Sperry, the GYROSCOPE pioneer, won a substantial prize offered for the first "hands-off" flight. The autopilot senses any deviation from the aircraft's flight pattern and automatically adjusts the ailerons, elevator and rudder to compensate for the deviation. The basis of the system is a GYROCOMPASS which controls the aircraft's direction, and vertical gyros which control pitch and roll.

Landing

Near an airport are the ILS (instrument landing system) beams used in air traffic control. Equipment on the plane uses the ground based localizer, marker and glidepath transmitters to guide the pilot to the airport and help in the landing procedure. Outer, middle and inner marker beacons give the distance from the runway threshold, the glidepath signals provide guidance on the correct angle of descent. The airport localizer beacon is picked up some 20 to 30 miles (30 to 50 km) away and the aircraft approaches to start the landing run at an altitude of some 1800 ft (550 m). When the glidepath signal is picked up the pilot follows this down, his progress being indicated by successive marker beacons. Visual and audible indications are given of the sequence of events and of any corrective action to be taken.

Weather radar

Most large commercial aircraft are fitted with weather radar which provides the flight crew with a picture of cloud formations and other atmospheric

Left: A pilot's eye view of one of the most sophisticated fighter aircraft – the British Aerospace Sea Harrier shows (1) radar controller (2) nozzle lever (3) flap selector (4) radio (5) HUD (6) engine speed and temperature gauges (7) weapons control (8) warning lights (9) head-up display (10) instruments (11) missile control panel (12) radar screen (13) fuel gauge (14) radar warning receiver (15) electronics panel (16, 17, 18) target identification unit (19) navigation and communication computers and associated switch gear.

disturbances ahead. The equipment consists of a forward looking radar mounted in the nose of the aircraft and a display unit on the flight deck. The radar scanner can be tilted downwards to provide ground mapping as an extra navigation aid when crossing coast lines, estuaries or other prominent geographical features. For weather radar, ranges of up to 300 miles (480 km) are possible. Good interpretation of the radar picture depends to some extent on the skill and experience of the crew.

Head up displays

Head up displays (HUD) project essential flight information in the form of images onto a combining glass in the pilot's forward line of sight. (This instrument is so named because the pilot can both see through it and read information presented on it.) The images appear to be at infinity, so that the pilot has no need to change the focus of his eyes. In effect, the data is superimposed on the landscape.

The systems were first used for the INERTIAL GUIDANCE of long range missiles where it is essential to have a system that cannot, as with radio guidance systems, be jammed by an enemy. They use gyroscopes and ACCELEROMETERS to detect changes in direction and velocity. A microminiature computer is used to calculate the present position which may be displayed as numbers or on a moving map. An inertial navigation system can have a number of other functions, such as providing steering signals for the autopilot to maintain preplanned routes.

Direction finding

Most aircraft still carry automatic direction finding (ADF) equipment for finding their position in areas where there is poor coverage by other systems. They use a simple loop antenna which picks up transmis-

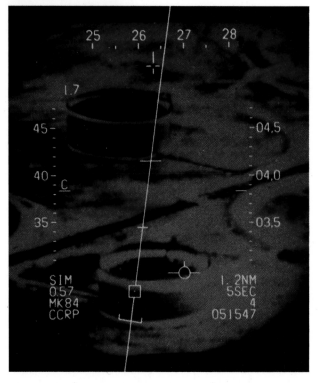

sions from radio beacons. The loop picks up the strongest signals from stations which are at right angles to it, so it can be used to find their direction.

An improvement on this very simple system is the VHF omnidirectional range (VOR). VOR transmitters radiate a VHF radiobeam which rotates in the same way as the light beam from a lighthouse. It does this 30 times a second, while transmitting a signal which varies at 30 Hz, so that each rotation of the beam corresponds to a single cycle of the transmission. Another transmission, which does

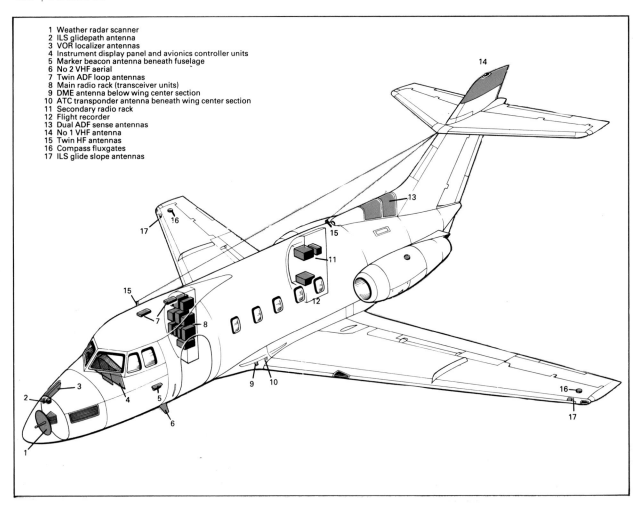

1 Weather radar scanner
2 ILS glidepath antenna
3 VOR localizer antennas
4 Instrument display panel and avionics controller units
5 Marker beacon antenna beneath fuselage
6 No 2 VHF aerial
7 Twin ADF loop antennas
8 Main radio rack (transceiver units)
9 DME antenna below wing center section
10 ATC transponder antenna beneath wing center section
11 Secondary radio rack
12 Flight recorder
13 Dual ADF sense antennas
14 No 1 VHF antenna
15 Twin HF antennas
16 Compass fluxgates
17 ILS glide slope antennas

not rotate, is sent out at the same frequency, so arranged that the two are in phase when the rotating beam points to magnetic north, on which all navigation systems are based. Equipment on the aircraft is tuned to the VHF transmission, and receives the two signals which will be out of phase to an extent which depends on their direction. By coupling this direction information to the autopilot, the plane will fly automatically to the beacon. VOR beacons are located at suitable intervals along established air corridors.

Distance measuring equipment (DME) and tactical air navigation (TACAN) are also available on busy routes, and use airborne interrogator-receiver equipment. Simple DME systems transmit a signal to a ground radio beacon, automatically triggering a reply signal. The time interval between the original transmitted pulse and the reply is directly related to distance and is read off by the receiver in nautical miles. TACAN is a military form of DME and normally gives the beacon's direction as well as its range.

TACAN is also used air to air to give range and direction between suitably equipped co-operating aircraft. Ranges of DME and TACAN are typically 200 miles (320 km).

Doppler navigators have been developed for use in addition to Loran-type systems. The DOPPLER EFFECT is the change in pitch of waves – such as sound, light or radio waves – as their source approaches or recedes. It is most often noticed when a car goes past at speed, the pitch of the sound of its engine being higher as it approaches and lower as it goes away.

In the case of a Doppler navigator, a microwave radio signal of known frequency is sent downwards to the Earth's surface. It is reflected back at a slightly different frequency, since the ground is moving relative to the aircraft, and this difference is measured to give the speed.

Doppler systems are entirely self-contained and can be programed to provide information on the distance and time, to go to preselected points on the route, to show latitude and longitude, to operate the pilot's steering indicator, or to drive moving map display systems. These, combined with color cathode ray display systems, go a long way to presenting essential information clearly.

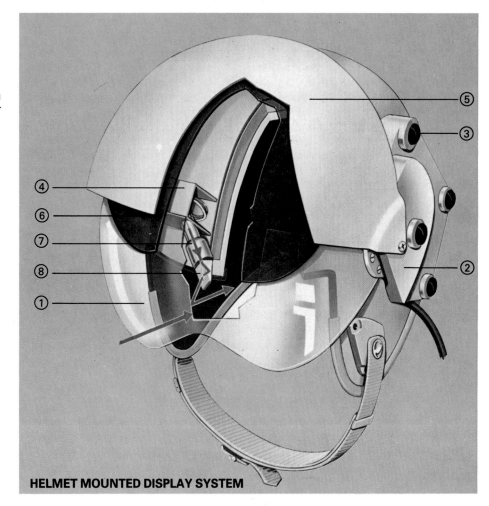

Left: The major avionic components in a Hawker Siddely 125 series 400 executive jet: (1) weather radar scanner (2) ILS glidepath antenna (3) VOR localizer antennas (4) instrument display panel (5) marker beacon antenna (6) no 2 VHF antenna (7) twin ADF loop antenna (8) transceiver units (9) DME antenna (10) ATC transponder antenna (11) secondary radio rack (12) flight recorder (13) dual ADF sense antennas (14) no 1 VHF antenna (15) twin HP antennas (16) compass fluxgates (17) ILS glide slope antennas.
Right: A helmet-mounted display system consisting of (1) clear visor combiner (2) visor latch mechanism (3) helmet position sensor leds (4) helmet electronics (5) visor cover (6) sun visor (7) led array (8) prism

HELMET MOUNTED DISPLAY SYSTEM

Inertial navigation

Aircraft flying long distances often do not use Loran or Doppler navigators, but instead use *inertial navigation systems* (INS), which are entirely self-contained. They work on the principle that if all changes of direction and velocity from the starting point are measured, then the position at any time can be calculated.

Today, nearly all autopilots have electrically driven gyros. Even the simplest autopilot will keep the aircraft on a selected heading in level flight far more accurately than a human pilot and this is still the autopilot's main function, but through the years many refinements have been added. Turns may be selected by the pilot through his autopilot: if a new altitude is chosen, the aircraft will climb or descend automatically until it has been reached; and the autopilot may be coupled to radio navigation systems (see below) so that the aircraft will automatically home on to a radio beacon or lock on to an instrument landing system.

A modern addition to the autopilot is the *autothrottle* which provides automatic speed control throughout the cruise, descent and final approach.

Navigation devices

The navigation equipment on an aircraft may be entirely self-contained, operating without any external aid or it may work in conjunction with ground based aids such as radio beacons and area radio navigation systems.

When an aircraft is flying between airports, it may use a system such as Loran, Decca Navigator or Omega. Each of these employs its own network of fixed ground stations which radiate a pattern of radio signals. From this, positions can be determined by measuring time or phase differences between the radio stations. The same signals are used by ships, and these systems are dealt with more fully in the article on navigation.

Loran (Long Range Air Navigation) is widely used by aircraft on long distance routes. Omega uses a much lower frequency, 10 to 14 kHz, and is being brought into use mainly because its signals will penetrate underwater.

See also: Accelerometer; Aerospace industry; Aircraft; Airplane; Airport; Air traffic control; Doppler effect; Gyroscope; Head-up display.

Baggage handling

Baggage handling is recognized as one of the major sources of problems in airline operations. Worldwide, about two million individual items are handled each day, and compensation must be paid to passengers for any which are lost. With the encouragement of world airlines and airport authorities suitable baggage handling equipment has been developed which largely uses conveyers. Passenger baggage comes in an infinite variety of shapes and sizes with not only suitcases made of varied materials, but also backpacks, duffel bags, folding strollers, skis, golf clubs and various boxes. Many also have loose straps and labels and some are tied with rope or string.

Three recent factors have compounded the difficulties of baggage conveyer manufacturers: the introduction of wide bodied jet airliners capable of carrying 300 to 500 passengers has brought into use mini-containers holding about 1000 individual units which must be quickly and accurately handled; increasing air traffic has resulted in airport terminals with departure and arrival gates far removed from the main building and its check-in or check-out points, leading to long and often complicated conveyer systems; and multi-level terminals may require baggage to be lifted or lowered through vertical distances of 40 ft (12 m) or more, without making heavy demands on expensive floor space or destroying the visual appeal of the building.

Handling methods

Any arrangement for conveying baggage must carry individual items without damaging them or removing or damaging their destination labels, and guide each unit quickly and efficiently to its terminal point. The system should also be unobtrusive and quiet.

Early conveying systems were simple, short and usually served only two points within the airport terminal. A modern system, handling outbound baggage however, will accept items from dozens of check-in points and deliver them to any of several aircraft loading points. The new Terminal 4 at Britain's Heathrow Airport has 64 check-in desks with 8 primary conveyers to 4 automatic tilt tray sorters. There are separate conveyers for nonstandard baggage. The Terminal capacity is 2000 passengers an hour in each direction, using 22 aircraft stands on a continuous basis.

Airport baggage handling can be divided into

Below: The Baggage Hall is where tired travelers are most likely to show their frustrations at depressing, long waits. Sometimes delays are caused by offloading problems at the airplane.

three phases: arrival and acceptance; conveyance within the building; and delivery to the aircraft or the passenger. Outbound the first phase involves identification of the flight and destination of the bag, usually from the passenger's ticket. The bag could be going to any one of several stops on the aircraft's route.

At larger international airports; passengers place their own bags on short conveyers mounted on electronic weigh scales. Check-in personnel do not handle the bags, and after reading the weight the bags are moved to short addressing conveyers and given a tie-on destination tag. Transfer of bags to dispatch conveyers is initiated by programable controllers which ensure that bags from any check-in desk can be conveyed with equal priority, without causing jams, in the shortest possible time. They are conveyed to the Baggage Hall where they are sorted manually by flight number and destination or if automatic sorting systems are used, are guided by equipment in the system to their aircraft loading positions by the stands.

Baggage from incoming flights is loaded on to a conveyer which takes it to a point in the main terminal building, where baggage belonging to passengers in transit is taken from the incoming plane to join that of the connecting flight.

Automatic systems are of considerable interest to operators at big, busy airports because they help to reduce high labor costs, as well as speeding up the flow of baggage. A relatively simple method of controlling a bag from a check-in point to its aircraft loading position is to attach a bar code sticker. Controlling scanners in the conveyer system read the code and route each bag to its destination.

Conveyers

Three main forms of conveyer are used at airports for moving baggage. An airport baggage complex may use one or more methods in a complete system as each has advantages and disadvantages. Belts made of heavy duty rubber or multi-layer flexible materials provide good, nonslip surfaces for straight runs, but modified belt units have to be provided at corners and bends.

A second method involves the use of pallets or plates linked together to form a continuous moving flat surface. Pallet conveying systems are designed which can follow very complicated routes. Each pallet is formed from molded rubber or plastic and will withstand the considerable shock loads of weights dropped on to them – 75 lb (34 kg) released from 18 in. (46 cm) is typical.

The third method is to provide individual trays, each of which carries one bag. The trays, which move in a continuous chain, can be programed to tip their contents when they reach a predetermined point in the system.

Above: The curve of this chute is designed to allow the baggage to slide quickly between floors without being damaged by impact.

Tipping trays provide one method of changing the path of a bag, for example, from the main conveyer to a collecting point. Other commonly used methods include arms or plows which, on demand, move across the conveyer to intercept a bag and divert it. Another way is to tilt a conveyer belt causing the bags to run along a fence. Parts of the fence can be opened to allow individual bags to fall through on to a chute.

Powered or gravity roller conveyers, which are used in warehouse systems, have a very limited use with airport baggage because items such as backpacks may stick on the rollers.

Some international airports have gateroom check-in at piers, which are built from the terminal onto the airport apron. Late passengers take their bags to the gateroom where they are placed on a spiral chute which conveys them to apron level. These stainless steel chutes are profiled to control the rate of baggage descent.

See also: Airplane; Airport; Bulk handling; Container handling; Conveyer; Electric motor; Fork lift truck; Plastics; Warehousing.

Bailey bridge

Early in World War II it became apparent that existing military bridges were becoming obsolete because the latest armored vehicles were too heavy to use them. The types of bridge used by the British army, for example, had a maximum span of 130 ft (40 m) and could not carry a load of more than 26 tons. Then in 1941, Sir Donald Bailey introduced a new design, which was easy to construct, adaptable, and capable of carrying up to 100 tons over spans of 220 ft (67 m). It was first used by the British in the North Africa campaign in 1942, and by the U.S. army in Europe from 1944; during the war American and British firms made 200 miles (322 km) of fixed and 40 miles (64 km) of floating Bailey equipment.

The basic Bailey bridge is made up of sections, each 10 ft (3 m) long, joined together to form a continuous span. Each section, known as a *bay,* has two side members (trusses) of girder construction, joined by cross pieces (transoms), which support the sheet metal roadway or *decking.* To increase the load capacity of the basic bridge, extra trusses and sometimes transoms are added to strengthen it. The bridge is easily transported since it is brought to the site in component form.

Floating Bailey bridge

For crossing rivers the Bailey bridge can be supported on large plywood floats known as *pontoons.* These are composed of three sections, each 20 ft (6 m) long, which are joined end to end to make one 60 ft (18 m) pontoon. The number of pontoons needed to support the bridge depends on the width of the river and the load to be carried. The floating part of the bridge is not one long rigid span, but is made up of 32 ft (10 m) lengths, each supported by a pontoon at either end with an additional one at the center for heavily loaded bridges. These sections are joined together by connectors which allow a certain amount of flexibility between them, to prevent excessive stress in the trusses as the pontoons rise and fall when a vehicle passes over them.

The end spans which connect the floating section to each bank are called truss hinge spans, and as their name implies they act rather like hinges in order to allow for any variation in the height of the river. The pontoons at the ends of the floating section are braced by a distributing girder because of the extra strain place upon them by the hinge spans.

As well as being useful during war – it is still in service with the U.S. army – the Bailey bridge has proved invaluable in peacetime; its great portability has been very useful in developing countries where it can dramatically improve communications. It has also seen service replacing bridges destroyed by accidents or swept away by floods. Development work still continues but the basic design has not radically altered from the original. An aluminum version was produced in the U.S. but it did not gain widespread acceptance, and steel is still the standard material used. Most of the improvements that have been made involve the methods of mechanized assembly.

See also: Aluminum; Bridge structure; Suspension bridge; Tank; Tracked vehicle.

Below: Bailey bridging can be used to span any desired width, without creating excess stresses, by placing crib piers at suitable intervals.

Balance

The balance is one of man's oldest measuring instruments, and was probably invented by the ancient Egyptians or Babylonians about 5000 BC. It was first used by them for weighing gold dust for jewellery, commercial goods being exchanged by barter rather than the payment of money for a weighed amount. These early balances consisted of a simple beam pivoted at its center, with standard weights in a pan at one end and the article to be weighed in a pan at the other. Even these early instruments were capable of weighing with a high degree of accuracy. Some in use in Egypt around 1350 BC were accurate to within 1 per cent.

The Romans made an important improvement to the design of balances when, at the point at which the beam is pivoted, they fixed a triangular section or "knife edge" *fulcrum* to the beam. This made the balance more sensitive and accurate especially when measuring very small weights.

The two pan balance

The two pan balance is probably the simplest and best known weighing device in the world. For every day use extreme accuracy is not usually necessary and a simple, robust balance is adequate, but when the weights involved are very small or require precise measurement, great care must be taken with the design and construction of the instrument to minimize errors. The beam is made from a rigid, light alloy, pivoted at its center on a synthetic sapphire knife edge which rests on a synthetic sapphire plate at the top of the central column of the balance. The pans hang from *stirrups* which are supported by synthetic sapphire plates resting on a knife edge at each end of the beam. A pointer, fixed to the center of the beam, extends to a scale which indicates when the beam is exactly horizontal, that is, when the weights in the two pans are equal.

The single pan mechanical balance

Instead of having a pan at each end of the beam, this balance has a fixed counterweight at one end and a pan and a set of built-in weights at the other, and when an item or material to be weighed is placed on the pan, some of the built-in weights are lifted clear of the beam until it balances again. The weight of the sample being measured is equal to the total of the weights removed, and as the total load on the beam is constant so is its sensitivity. The weights are added mechanically by turning knobs, which are mounted on the outside of the case. The beam pointer and scale are mounted at the end of the counterweight, and its movement is projected optically to the front of the case. The single pan balance was widely used in industrial, medical and research

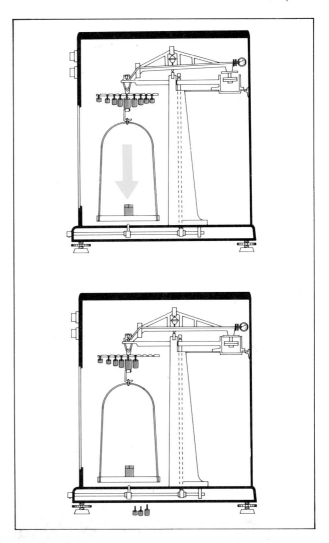

Above: The counterweight of the single pan or constant load balance exactly balances the pan and removable weights at the front.

laboratories throughout the world, until the advent of the electronic balance and the microchip.

Microbalances

A microbalance is a very accurate type of balance which can measure weight differences as small as one hundreth of a microgram.

Electronic microbalances measure by employing a moving coil mechanism similar to that used in an ammeter. In one form of this instrument, the beam is attached at one end to a coil, in the same way as the needle of an ammeter, with a small pan at the other end. If an object is placed in the pan the beam will tilt downwards from its horizontal position. The beam is restored to the horizontal by passing an electric current through the coil, and the current required is proportional to the amount of force needed to raise the beam. This analog current is measured, but it is calibrated in units of weight instead of current by microprocessors so that the weight of the sample can be read instantly.

The single pan electronic balance

Modern balances are classified into different types. *Microbalances* are used for very fine measurement, say of dust particles in the air and generally weigh amounts down to one millionth of a gram. *Semi-microbalances* are more common and are used in research practices where accuracies to five decimal places are required. *Analytical* balances weigh to 0.0001 g and are very common in research, education and general laboratory work. *Precision* balances are those which are generally accurate from 1 gram to 0.001 g and are very common. Any balance which is less accurate than 1 gram is normally known as a *scale*. These scales are widely used in factories and even stores and markets.

Just about all modern balances and scales are now electronic. They are more robust, smaller and much easier to use than the old mechanical balance. All electronic balances use an easily read digital display so there can be no mistakes when accuracy is needed.

For weighing in laboratories where an accuracy of 1 gram or better is needed most electronic balances use a very accurate measuring system. The principle employed is termed *Electromagnetic Force Compensation*. It is based on a simple physical theory – the electrodynamic right-hand rule. This states that if an electric current is passed through a wire which is located between the poles of a permanent magnet, a force is generated.

Electromagnetic Force Compensation is used where a high accuracy is needed because a very strict linear relationship exists between the current used and the force generated. To make an electronic balance you need a weighing pan, which is fixed to the wire in the magnetic field. The location of the wire must be controlled using an indicator. A regulated power source and a current measuring device are also required. When the pan has no load on it, the system keeps just enough current flowing through the wire to maintain the wire position indicator at its zero point. As weight is added, so the wire in the magnetic field is pushed down. The indicator registers this fact and tells the power regulator to put more current through the wire. Therefore the force generated is also increased. This continues until the position indicator is once again at its zero point. In practice all of this happens almost instantaneously. The difference in the current indicated by the measuring device between the loaded and unloaded condition is proportional to the weight placed on the pan.

The current measuring systems of electronic balances of high accuracy are very sophisticated microprocessors. They convert the electric signals produced into the easily read displays which we all see – even in the supermarkets.

See also: **Computer; Digital readout device; Electromagnetism; Weighing machine.**

Below: A Chinese engraving of 1811 showing a type of steelyard being used in a weighing shop.
Right: A digital analytical electronic balance which can weigh with accuracy to 0.0001 g.

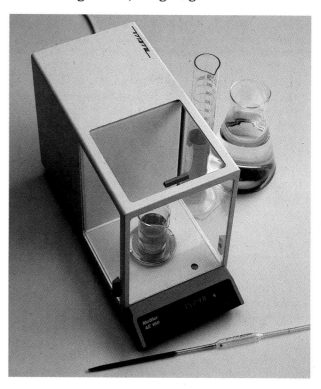

Ballistics

Ballistics is the study of projectiles and the extent to which their trajectories are affected by shape, propulsion system, gravity, temperature, wind etc. There are three branches: *interior*, dealing with all aspects of propulsion within a gun barrel or at launch; *exterior*, concerned with the trajectory of the projectile in flight; and *terminal*, relating to the effects of the missile on the target.

There are a great number of related factors which have their effect on interior ballistics. For a start there is the propellant and the task of measuring the pressure it exerts upon the projectile. This depends upon the density of the gas given off by the exploding propellant and the rate at which it burns. So internal ballistics is founded on THERMODYNAMIC principles and the advent of computers has enabled a more accurate determination of gun systems.

Besides the propellant there is the shape of the projectile and the characteristics of the gun to be taken into account in interior ballistics. Whether a gun is *rifled* or *smooth barreled* obviously makes a difference to the behavior of shot as does the efficiency of the weapon's recoil mechanism. It is also evident that, within limits, more muzzle velocity can be imparted to a light, large-diameter projectile than to a heavy small-diameter one.

The diameter of the projectile and all its aerodynamic properties is also the concern of exterior ballistics – as is its muzzle velocity. An illustration of this is the fact that, although higher muzzle velocity can be imparted to a light, large-diameter projectile, the aerodynamic drag upon it will reduce its velocity much more rapidly during flight than the velocity of a heavy, small-diameter projectile. An example of applying ballistics to get the best of both worlds is the discarding sabot principle by

Above: The aerodynamic properties of a bullet can be seen clearly in this high speed photograph of the projectile disturbing the waves of heat above a lighted candle.
Below left and right: The flight of a Copperhead shell, traveling faster than a missile, is captured by rotation prism cameras at the U.S. Army's White Sands Missile range in New Mexico.

which a light, large-diameter case is employed to carry a heavy, small-diameter shot out of a gun muzzle to reduce drag during flight.

In the same way, rifling a projectile causes it to spin during flight and is a means of stabilizing it to prevent it toppling, which would increase the drag on it. The other main force operating on a missile in the exterior phase is gravity.

Terminal ballistics grows more and more detailed and complex as the task demanded of projectiles becomes more varied. The business of penetrating armor for instance has resulted in types of shot with different terminal characteristics. There is shot which uses kinetic energy and is essentially a long, strong, thin round hurled with maximum velocity at an armored target and there is shot which uses chemical energy or shaped explosive which detonates on the target and blasts through it or causes it to *scab*. The boundaries of terminal ballistics were only extended in this way because more sophisticated measuring instruments enabled the phenomena taking place to be observed in milliseconds.

Another aspect of terminal ballistics is *wound ballistics* or the study of damage caused to the human body by ammunition. This can be useful in law enforcement as the direction and range of a shot can be gauged from the wound it makes. For military purposes wound ballistics concentrates on producing the maximum human damage for the force expended. An *assymetrical bullet* will tumble more quickly when it reaches the target and so cause an increasing wound effect – the hollow-nosed *Loffelspitz*.

See also: Ammunition; Bullet; Gun.

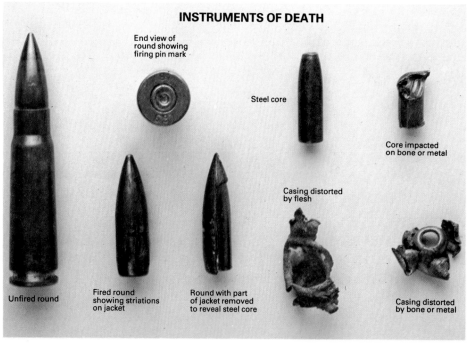

INSTRUMENTS OF DEATH

End view of round showing firing pin mark

Steel core

Core impacted on bone or metal

Casing distorted by flesh

Unfired round

Fired round showing striations on jacket

Round with part of jacket removed to reveal steel core

Casing distorted by bone or metal

Above: The next battlefield will be low earth orbits where missiles will be targeted onto enemy missiles and satellited between 93 miles (150 km) and 22,000 miles (35,000 km) above the globe.
Left: A rifle round from a Soviet Kalashnikov AK-47 before and after firing and meeting with different types of target. It has a steel core, a soft lead tip and a cupro-nickel casing. The identification of either a bullet or a gun connected with a violent crime is one of the most basic functions of forensic ballistics.

Balloon

Balloons are unique in that they are the only form of aircraft which spans the entire history of flight. They were the means by which man first took to the air and they are still in use today.

The first manned flight took place by means of a hot-air balloon, on November 21 1783. The balloon, made by the Montgolfier brothers Joseph and Etienne, paper manufacturers, was 75 ft (23 m) high by nearly 50 ft (15 m) in diameter – a frail affair of cloth backed with paper and heated by a furnace burning chopped straw. The pilots were Pilatre de Rozier and the Marquis d'Arlandes.

Only a few weeks later Jacques Charles, also French, made the first ascent in a hydrogen filled balloon, and almost at once the gas balloon established itself as superior to the hot-air version. Although it took longer to inflate it was quiet, easier to handle, lifted more, and above all could be used again. The hot-air balloons had a tendency, not surprisingly, to set themselves alight or at least to finish their flights in a charred and brittle condition; neither of which were endearing features.

The use of hydrogen balloons grew unchecked until the development of airships. They proved useful in both research and war, in the latter particularly as military observation platforms, for which purpose they were used by both sides in the American Civil War and again in World War I. They were generally captive type balloons, anchored to the ground by long cables. In sport, they reached their peak in the famous Gordon Bennett races which took place in Europe between 1906 and 1938, in which the greatest distance covered was 1368 miles (2191 km).

Apart from their importance in military reconnaissance, balloons were also used for bombing. In 1849 the Austrians loaded paper hot-air balloons with small bombs and released them so that they drifted towards Venice. In 1944 the Japanese again

Below: At 40,000 ft (12,200 m) the night air is −58° F (−50° C) and the jet streams at this altitude can average a speed of 100 mph (160 kph).

Above: A hydrogen-filled Caquot kite balloon of the type used during World War II to support cables as a screen against low-flying aircraft.

used the same device when they released hydrogen-filled paper balloons loaded with bombs in the direction of Canada and the U.S. In the latter stages of World War I the early mono and biplanes gradually replaced the balloon for aerial observations. The balloon made a comeback, however, in World War II when barrage balloons were used to protect ships and cities from aerial attack.

In 1955 a significant development took place in the U.S. which was to revive ballooning as a sport. The U.S. Navy was at that time operating *blimps* (small airships) for offshore patrols, and pilots were being trained on gas balloons. In an attempt to cut costs, the Navy sponsored a program to develop hot-air balloons and this culminated in a practical design being produced by a company in South Dakota in 1963. The Navy lost interest in the project, but the company decided to market the design as a sporting balloon, and the modern re-usable hot-air balloon was born. Hot-air balloons are now manufactured in varying sizes from 30,000 to 140,000 cu ft (850 to 3964 m³) to carry from one to six people or an equivalent load.

Principle of balloon flight

A balloon is a lighter than air unpowered aircraft. Unlike heavier than air machines such as airplanes and gliders, which stay airborne by moving through the air to create dynamic lift, a balloon obtains its lift by displacement, which is a static force and does not require movement through the air to create it. An airship is fitted with one or more engines and also with controls (rudder and elevators), but a balloon has no engine and cannot be steered: it merely drifts with the wind. The study of the science of ballooning is called *aerostatics*.

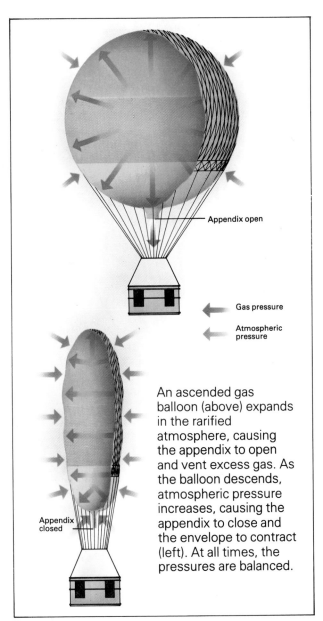

Appendix open

Gas pressure

Atmospheric pressure

Appendix closed

An ascended gas balloon (above) expands in the rarified atmosphere, causing the appendix to open and vent excess gas. As the balloon descends, atmospheric pressure increases, causing the appendix to close and the envelope to contract (left). At all times, the pressures are balanced.

the molecules in the air, that is, they have a lower density than air. Hot air is lighter than cold air because any gas (and air is a gas) expands when heated. The molecules are driven further apart and therefore a given volume will contain a lower weight of molecules. At sea level 1000 cu ft (28 m³) of air at 212° F (100° C) will have a lifting capacity of 17.4 lb (7.9 kg) when the surrounding air is at 60° F (16° C). A similar amount of helium has a lifting capacity of 65 lb (29.5 kg), and for hydrogen the lift available is 70 lb (31.75 kg).

From the point of view of lift alone, it is obvious that the best thing to fill a balloon with is hydrogen and the worst is hot air. Ordinary coal gas can be, and has been, used to fill balloons. Its disadvantage is that it varies considerably in purity; the lift obtainable is therefore very unpredictable. The domestic gas of today weighs more than the gas available in the early days of ballooning. All lifting media have advantages and disadvantages. Gases are expensive, since they have to be extracted from the air and transported. It costs considerably more to inflate a hydrogen balloon than it does to inflate a hot-air balloon. Hydrogen is highly flammable, but helium, which is safer because it neither burns nor forms explosive mixtures with air, is much more expensive than hydrogen in most countries, except however, the U.S.

These factors aside, there are other aspects of gas and hot air which have resulted in the development of two distinct types of balloon, different in design, performance, and to some extent in the manner in which they are controlled.

Gas balloons

Hydrogen easily penetrates most materials and the fabric of a hydrogen balloon envelope is therefore quite heavy, about half the total weight of the balloon, made from fabric impregnated with rubber or neoprene. The envelope is spherical, the most efficient shape to contain a given volume, and is contained in a string net which distributes the load evenly over the fabric. Below the envelope, the net is drawn together at a load ring, from which a basket to carry crew and equipment is suspended.

The envelope is not sealed: at the bottom is a long narrow open tube called the *appendix*. As the balloon rises, atmospheric pressure decreases and the gas in the balloon expands. The appendix allows gas to escape, thus preventing the balloon from bursting as a result of its internal pressure. When the balloon descends, the appendix closes (like a wet drinking straw if it is sucked too hard). This prevents air from getting into the balloon and forming an explosive mixture with the hydrogen.

To ascend in a hydrogen balloon it is necessary to reduce weight by discharging ballast in the form of sand, since lift cannot be increased. Similarly in

A balloon is in equilibrium, that is, balanced in the air and not moving up or down, when its total weight is the same as the weight of the volume of air it is occupying, or displacing. Since the fabric, basket, crew, and equipment are all heavier than air, they must be balanced by filling the envelope with some gas lighter than air. When the difference between the weight of the gas in the envelope and the outside air is the same as the weight of all the components making up the balloon, the balloon will be in equilibrium.

Gases which are lighter than air, and therefore suitable for filling a balloon include hydrogen, helium, and ordinary air which has been heated. Some gases are lighter than air because the weight of their molecules is less than the average weight of

order to descend it is necessary to reduce lift, since additional ballast cannot be obtained while airborne. This is done by opening a small valve in the top of the balloon; the valve is operated by a cord down to the basket and is held shut by springs or elastic. The height to which a balloon can rise is limited because the density of the atmosphere decreases (the air becomes thinner) as the height above sea level increases. Therefore, as the balloon rises, the air around it becomes less dense, until it reaches a height at which the atmospheric density is as low as the total density of the balloon. At this point, as the densities are equal, the balloon is in equilibrium with the surrounding air and will not rise any farther.

The small valve and the ballast are the only forms of control in a gas balloon. Once the balloon is in equilibrium, they will not need to be used much unless the balloon is affected by outside factors such as a general cooling or heating of the outside air, which will cause the lifting gas to contract or expand. Gas balloons, therefore, have very good endurance. On the other hand, every maneuver in a gas balloon is a wasting process: even to descend it is necessary to get rid of gas.

Operationally, then, the main advantages of gas balloons are endurance and lifting power. The main disadvantages are the cost and inconvenience of inflating the balloon, a process which can take as long as two hours.

Hot-air balloons

Modern hot-air balloons are almost the only really significant design development to have taken place since balloons were invented. Despite their relatively poor lifting power and endurance, they have been responsible for a tremendous upsurge in the sport because of their low running costs, their simplicity, and their safety.

Structurally a hot-air balloon is quite different from a gas balloon. Hot air cannot penetrate fabrics in the way that hydrogen can: the envelope is there-

Gas valve

Ripping panel for deflation on landing

Gas-containing fabric (laminated nylon and metallized Melinex)

Helium space

Ripping line

Valve line

ICI

Inflation and overflow tube

Balloon cruises in the jet stream

Cirrus cloud streaks

Rainstorms

Clear skies

Axis of polar front jet-stream 90 knots at 30,000 ft

Rainstorms

Widespread and partial cover convective clouds

N   500 miles

Low level balloon track
20 knot speed at 2000 ft

Left: Innovation is the name of the balloon planned for the first circumnavigation of the globe and is expected to be capable of speeds up to 100 mph (160 kph) through the jet streams. The 200 ft (60 m) high envelope – a thin plastic and nylon laminate – has a maximum capacity of more than a million cu ft and is filled with a mixture of hot air and helium. During the sunlight hours the helium expands to fill the envelope, and by night a turbine generator on top of the gondola pumps hot air. The twin-level solar heated aluminum gondola is fully pressurized.

Far left: The revival of hot-air ballooning owes its origins to Ed Yost, an employee of the U.S. company General Mills who were contracted, because they could make polyethylene, to produce lightweight balloons first for Radio Free Europe and later for the U.S. Navy. Yost built and launched hydrogen balloons but found their small payload of about 10 lb (4.5 kg) unsatisfactory. To increase the payload he attached a plumber's blowtorch to the neck of a 8000 cu ft (225 cu m) balloon which, in 1953, gave flight to a new generation of hot-air balloons.

Left: Almost every country in the world sends up gas-filled radiosonde (remote meteorological) balloons twice daily to gather weather information.

fore made of very light material, usually rip-proof nylon treated with polyurethane to reduce porosity.

The profile of a hot-air balloon is termed *natural shape*: wide at the top tapering toward the bottom in the shape naturally created by the internal pressure. Loads are carried on nylon tapes sewn into and integral with the envelope. From these tapes, steel wires lead down to the burner, which is in the same position as the load ring on a gas balloon.

The basket is suspended from the burner by steel wires or a rigid structure, depending on the manufacturer. At the base of the balloon there is a large opening to allow heat from the burner to enter. A modern hot-air balloon burner uses propane, which is fed under its own bottle pressure to the burner jets. The heat generated may be anything from 8 to 25 million Btu (approximately 3 to 5 GJ) per hour, much more than many industrial space heaters.

Hot-air balloons are fundamentally different from gas balloons in that it is possible to increase or decrease the lift simply by heating the air or allowing it to cool. Ballast and valve are therefore not strictly necessary. When flying a hot-air balloon the pilot simply turns on the burner if he wants to ascend, and leaves it off and allows the air to cool if

he wants to descend. The air in fact takes some time to cool, and the burner can be left off for quite long periods before the balloon starts to lose height. With the average sized balloon of between 50,000 and 90,000 cu ft inflation can be accomplished in a matter of minutes and this compensates for the relatively poor endurance of hot-air balloons (up to five or six hours depending on the load), since several flights can be made in a single day.

Scientific balloons

Unmanned gas-filled balloons are used extensively for weather observation and scientific research. Weather balloons carry instruments which collect information on atmospheric conditions such as temperature, pressure, and humidity. In older balloons, this information may be recorded on graphs, in which case the instrument pack must be recovered before the graph can be read.

Balloons are used to carry a wide range of scientific instruments into the upper atmosphere, including telescopes and cameras for astronomical research. They are employed in research into such things as pollution of the upper atmosphere, cosmic rays, and meteorites. One such experiment used a system of two interconnected balloons, one large and one small, to lift a 13,000 lb (5896 kg) payload.

More frequently used are weather balloons which are carried round the earth by circulating winds at a height of over 15 miles (24 km) carrying payloads of 90 lb (41 kg). These balloons are about 65 ft (20 m) in diameter made from a double layer of Mylar (a polyester film) 0.02 in. (0.5 mm) thick.

Designers and aero-engineers are constantly attempting to advance the frontiers of ballooning, and to reduce size and cost. Hot air is still relatively difficult to fly because balloons are so big. Manufacturers are experimenting with modern materials such as KEVLAR, which can resist heat up to temperatures of 750° F (400° C). It's a very expensive fabric – and so tough it cannot be cut with a pair of scissors, but a Kevlar balloon would lift four times the weight of a conventional balloon, and that means balloons could be a quarter of their present size. However, it would be very wasteful of heat, because there is such a large difference between the inside and outside temperature. Kevlar balloons would have to be insulated to keep the heat inside.

Experiments are also being made with low energy balloons, which are much bigger. There is a solar-heated balloon with a transparent top and a black bottom, which absorbs and radiates the heat. The solar energy comes in from the top, hitting the black bottom and reradiating the heat into the center of the balloon. The balloon is inflated with a fan and burner, but once aloft is capable of indefinite flight.

See also: Air; Aircraft; Aluminum; Aviation; Kevlar; Pressure; Temperature.

• FACT FILE •

- In August 1978 Double Eagle II was the first balloon to make a successful crossing of the Atlantic, carrying a crew of three. The flight took 137 hours and 6 minutes, leaving Presque Isle in Maine on August 11, and touching down to the west of Paris on August 17. The balloon was made of a neoprene-coated polyamide fabric, and had a capacity of 160,000 cubic feet (4531 cubic meters).

- Prior to the development of sophisticated satellites, unmanned balloons working at great altitude were used to study planets. Stratoscope II observed Mars from 77,000 ft (23,470 m) through a 36 in. (91 cm) reflecting telescope. Stratoscope II also carried a camera, which was used to take the first clear photograph of Uranus.

- Some scientific and meteorological balloons are designed to burst at a given altitude, their instrument package returning to Earth by parachute. They expand from 5 ft (1.5 m) diameter on inflation, to about 20 ft (6 m) diameter before bursting, at a daytime altitude of some 100,000 ft (30,480 m), which reduces to 80,000 ft (24,384 m) at night.

Left: The capacity of hot-air balloons is ever increasing. The world's largest standard production model in 1980 had a 140,000 cu ft (3960 cu m) intake, and could carry eight people. The envelope fabric must be non-porous and proofed against the deteriorating effects of ultraviolet light. Rip stop polyamide is the most popular material but manufacturers are now experimenting with alternative materials such as Kevlar; although very expensive it is very tough, and can lift about four times the weight.

Ballpoint pen

The ballpoint pen is the universal writing instrument of the twentieth century. When the tiny metal ball at the writing tip is drawn across a sheet of paper, it rotates within a housing at the end of an ink reservoir and is coated with the ink which it transfers to the paper.

The first ballpoint pen was invented by an American, John Loud, in 1888. Loud had been working on a design for a non-leaking pen to mark leather and fabrics and, although his cumbersome design was similar in essence to the modern item, it was never manufactured in large quantities and the patent was allowed to expire. The first workable design was patented by a pair of Hungarian brothers, Laszlo and Georg Biro in 1938. At the outbreak of World War II they moved to Argentina and began licensing the invention to several countries. The impetus for wide American acceptance came in 1942 when the U.S. army demanded a pen that would not leak in high-flying aircraft.

The ball of the pen is usually made of tungsten carbide and is normally one millimeter in diameter. It is fitted into a socket so that it rotates freely. Several internal ducts in the socket feed ink to the ball which therefore effectively rests on several metal ridges. The other end of the socket is drilled and fitted onto a metal or plastic tube which contains the ink. When the ball is pressed on paper and moved, the capillary action draws the ink from the reservoir, and impressions are made as the ink flows down the ducts. In effect, the ball functions as a valve to prevent overflow, and on rotation it acts as a suction pump drawing out the ink.

One problem was that as some of the ink ran out, a partial vacuum was formed between the back of the ball and the ink reservoir, which cut off the supply. This was solved by making a small hole at the far end of the reservoir. As the ink at the tip is sucked out, more ink from the tube is drawn into the socket to fill its place, the vacuum being prevented by air which is drawn in through the vent.

This method of inking the ballpoint pen depended on finding an ink that was susceptible to capillary action but which would not leak from the vent. At first, printer's ink was used but it was soon discovered that it was not viscous enough to prevent leakage. Therefore the principal research into making an efficient ballpoint pen in the last thirty years has been concerned with developing a suitable ink. The earliest ballpoint inks were of a heavy gelatinous type, but now there are two main kinds. The first, containing a dye soluble in oil, dries on the writing surface by absorption. The viscosity of the ink is high but the impressions formed tend to be less sharp than those created by spirit-soluble inks which dry on the writing surface by evaporation.

The capacity of the ballpoint reservoir varies fom 0.5 to 1.5 milliliters. In the smaller reservoirs the tube is open at the far end as the viscosity of the ink is sufficient to prevent leakage, but 1.5 ml reservoirs need a vented plug and the use of an even more viscous liquid known as a *follower*. The follower is solid enough not to leak but liquid enough to follow the ink as it is used up.

While the efficiency and reliability of even disposable ballpoints has improved considerably since 1938, two further improvements have recently been made. The first is the production of a pen that writes at any angle, even upside down. The second development is a new ink which is erasable.

See also: Aniline dye; Fountain pen; Ink; Paper; Printing; Viscosity.

Below: A drawing from the original patent specification for Lazlo and George Biro's ballpoint pen.

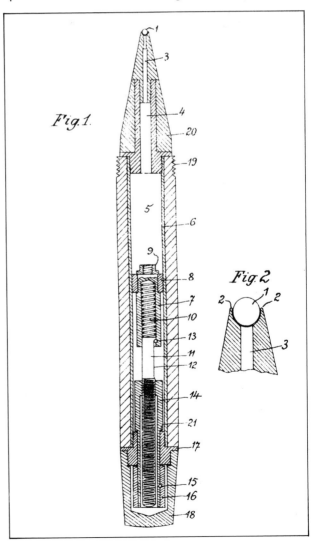

Barbed wire

Barbed wire, first patented in the U.S. in 1867, played an important part in the development of American farming, as it enabled the settlers to make effective fencing to enclose their land and keep cattle away from their crops. This had a considerable effect on cattle ranching, since the herds no longer had unrestricted use of the plains for grazing, and it led to conflict between the farmers and the cattlemen. Before barbed wire came into general use, fencing was often made from serrated wire, which was unsatisfactory because it broke

easily when under strain, and snapped in cold weather through contraction. The first practical machine for producing barbed wire (then also known as bob wire or devil's rope) was invented in 1874 by Illinois farmer Joseph Glidden, and between then and the end of the century about 400 types of barbed wire were devised, of which only about a dozen were ever put to practical use.

Types of barbed wire

Modern barbed wire is made from mild steel, high tensile steel, or aluminum. Mild steel and aluminum barbed wire have two strands twisted together to form a cable which is stronger than single-strand wire and less affected by temperature changes. Single-strand wire, of round or oval section, is made from high-tensile steel with the barbs crimped or welded on. A typical example of mild steel barbed wire would have two strands of 0.098 in. (2.5 mm) diameter, with the barbs made from 0.078 in. (2.0 mm) diameter wire, spaced 3.75 in. (95 mm) apart, with two or four points 0.5 in. (12.7 mm) long. The steel wires used are galvanized – coated with zinc to make them rustproof.

Production methods

The two wires which make up the line wire or cable are fed separately into the machine at one end. They leave it at the other end twisted together, barbed, and wound onto a reel. The wire to make the barbs is fed into the machine from the sides, from one side for two pointed barbs and from both sides for four pointed barbs. With the line wires twisted together and stationary in the machine, spinner heads wind the wire for the barbs around one or both strands (depending on the type of wire being made), and the barbs are cut to length by knives which cut diagonally through the wire to produce a sharp point. The line wire is then moved along the required distance so that the next barb can be wound on. This process continues automatically, and the finished barbed wire is wound on to reels (usually made of steel wire), in lengths of 440 yards (400 m) or in weights of up to 112 lb (50 kg).

As well as its uses in farming, barbed wire is used for security fences and for military purposes, the latter usually in the form of long coils or entanglements called concertina wire.

See also: Aluminum; Alloy; Drawing, of metal; Security systems; Wire and cable, manufacture.

Left: Coils of barbed wire around an antiaircraft missile installation give some protection against surprise attacks from the ground. The wire can be penetrated but, because it is inexpensive and easy to deploy, it serves a useful defense against all but the most determined attacker.

Barometer

Barometers are instruments for measuring atmospheric pressure. The atmosphere exerts a pressure because air has weight and is being pulled to the earth by the force of gravity. For this reason atmospheric pressure depends on the height of air above the point at which it is being measured and is lower on top of a mountain than it is at sea level.

Pressure is the force acting on a certain area and is commonly expressed in such units as pounds force per square inch (psi), newtons per square meter (N/m^2), pascals (Pa) and bars (sometimes millibars or mbar). Another common unit of pressure is the atmosphere, which is defined as the average atmospheric pressure at 32° F (0° C), sea level and 45° latitude. One atmosphere is approximately 14.7 psi, 101,325 N/m^2 or 1.01325 bar.

The pressure at the bottom of a container of gas or liquid can be determined in the above units from the height (h) of the container column, the density (d) of the gas or liquid, and the acceleration (g) due to gravity, all expressed in compatible units. The pressure is h x d x g. The width of the container does not affect the pressure – in the case of atmospheric pressure the container is worldwide

In atmospheric pressure measurement, a column of a standard liquid (one with known density) in a vertical tube is used and as gravity is approximately constant at all points on the Earth's surface, it is only necessary to record the column height. Mercury is the most common liquid used because it is extremely dense and so only needs a short column. One atmosphere is the pressure at the bottom of a column of mercury only 30 in. (760 mm) high. Consequently, one atmosphere pressure is often referred to as 30 in. (760 millimeters) of mercury (30 in. Hg or 760 mm Hg – Hg is the chemical symbol for mercury). Using water, whose density is about 1/13 that of mercury, one atmosphere is about 34 ft (10 m) of water.

Gases are not used because their densities are very much less than those of liquids and the column would have to be extremely tall. For example, normal atmospheric pressure would be the result of approximately five miles (8 km) of air, if its density were constant. There is, however, a further complication in that gases are compressible, while liquids are not, which means that the density increases with pressure.

Mercury barometers

The fact that the atmosphere has weight and exerts pressure was first demonstrated by the Italian scientist Galileo in the early seventeenth century. It was his pupil Torricelli, however, who worked out the actual working principle of the barometer.

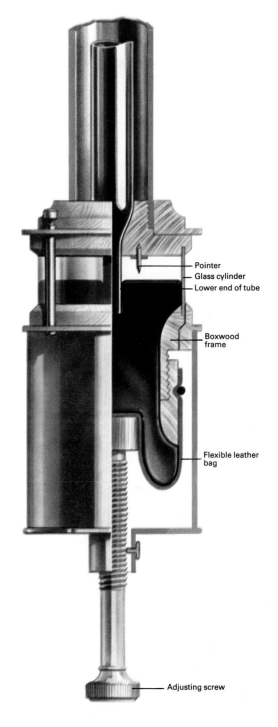

Pointer
Glass cylinder
Lower end of tube

Boxwood frame

Flexible leather bag

Adjusting screw

Above: The Fortin barometer – designed by Jean Fortin and first brought into use in the early nineteenth century. To obtain a reading the adjusting screw is turned, compressing the flexible leather bag until the mercury level in the cistern reaches the tip of the ivory pointer. The difference between the two mercury levels can then be read from the fixed scale and movable vernier – which increases the accuracy of the reading – by the column.

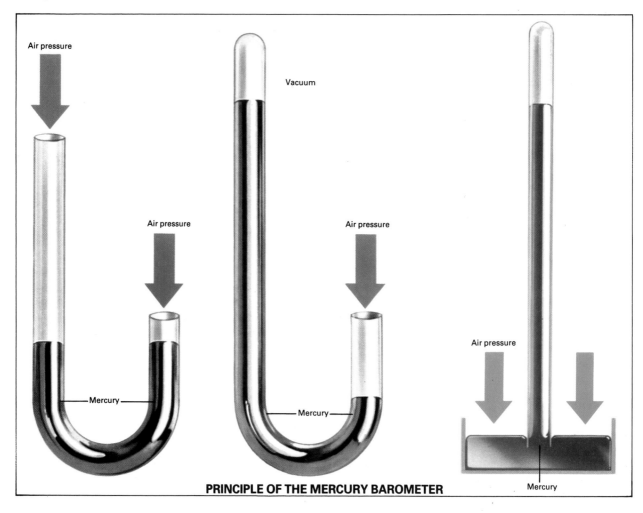

PRINCIPLE OF THE MERCURY BAROMETER

In principle, the weight of a column of mercury is balanced against the weight of the air. To do this, a glass tube more than 30 in. (760 mm) long, sealed at one end, is completely filled with mercury. This is then placed upright with its sealed end uppermost and its open end dipped into an open bowl of mercury. The pressure on the open surface of the mercury is the atmospheric pressure, and this must balance the pressure created by the column of mercury. The mercury level in the tube therefore falls until the weight of the column exactly balances the atmospheric pressure; by falling, it creates a vacuum at the top of the glass tube. The fact that the bottom of the tube is submerged prevents air from entering the tube, allowing the mercury to run out.

As the atmospheric pressure changes, so will the height of the mercury column, and by measuring its height above the surface of the open bowl, the atmospheric pressure can be found.

All modern mercury barometers are based on Torricelli's basic design, and only differ by a few modifications which enable more accurate and consistent readings to be made. Two important types of mercury barometer are the Fortin and the Kew.

Above: The operating principle of the mercury barometer. Left: Both ends of the tube are open and the atmospheric pressure is equal on both sides. Center: One tube is sealed and evacuated. The pressure now affects one side only. Right: The open end of the tube is replaced by a shallow dish and the closed end by a single inverted glass tube.

Fortin barometer

In the simple barometer mentioned above, any change in the column height will mean a slight change in the mercury level in the bowl. Yet, as it is from this level that the column height is measured, this would mean using a moving scale to find the height of the top of the column. The Fortin barometer overcomes this problem by employing an adjustable container (called a cistern) so that the open mercury level can be raised or lowered to a fixed point. This point is where the mercury level just touches a fixed ivory pointer. The column height is then measured with a fixed vertical scale. For even more accurate readings an adjustable VERNIER scale is added, which allows readings to be measured to within 0.002 in. (0.05 mm) of mercury.

Kew barometers

The Kew barometer has a fixed cistern and allowance is made for changes in the open mercury level by altering the spacing of the column scale. If both the column and the cistern are perfectly cylindrical then the change in the column scale compared to the true inch or millimeter will always be in a fixed ratio. This ratio is made very close to equality by making the barometer column very narrow compared with the diameter of the cistern.

Kew barometers are often used in ships, where motion can affect the accuracy of the readings by causing oscillations in the mercury column. This is overcome by introducing a restriction in the column which dampens such oscillations without unduly affecting the sensitivity of the device.

A further modification is an air trap to prevent any air from entering the column from the cistern and reaching the vacuum at the top of the tube, which might happen if the barometer was tilted or shaken. Kew barometers are designed to be portable, usually being carried upside down with the mercury completely filling the glass tube.

Aneroid barometer

It was another Italian scientist, Lucius Vidie, who in 1843 invented the aneroid barometer. The term "aneroid" means without liquid, and although not offering quite the same degree of sensitivity or accuracy as the mercury type, it has the advantage of being a robust instrument useful in such applications as altimeters, and generally where mobility is required (an aneroid altimeter is exactly the same machine as a barometer, and is used to measure height by air pressure).

The principle of the aneroid barometer is that a sealed metal chamber, sometimes called the bellows, expands and contracts with changes in atmospheric pressure. This expansion and contraction can be suitably amplified with a rack-and-pinion arrangement or levers to move a pointer on a suitably graduated scale.

The chamber is usually made of thin sheet nickel-silver alloy or hardened and tempered steel. High grade aneroid barometers have a series of steel diaphragms formed into a complete unit and corrugated to provide greater flexibility.

Temperature compensation is necessary with precision aneroid barometers, since the diaphragms expand and contract with temperature changes, and their elasticity alters. Any air within the chamber also leads to unwanted temperature effects from expansion and contraction, and so a high vacuum is generally created in the chamber.

The modern aneroid barometer is a precision instrument, which, when compensation is introduced for temperature and other errors, can easily give pressure readings to within 0.02 in. Hg (0.5 mm Hg) and can be estimated to within 0.001 in. Hg (0.025 mm Hg). When used as an altimeter this means height readings estimated to within one foot (30 cm) at sea level, and 1.5 ft (45 cm) at 11,000 ft (3350 m) where the air is thinner. Altimeters must be adjusted before use to take account of the prevailing air pressure in the area.

Aneroid barograph

A refinement of the aneroid barometer is the aneroid barograph, a self-recording barometer for meteorological and aeronautical applications where a continuous record of pressure variations is required. Instead of a pointer, a pen is attached which traces a graph on chart paper wrapped around a slowly revolving drum.

Because of the friction between the pen and the paper, its accuracy is not quite as good as the aneroid barometer. For better sensitivity, a refined version known as a microbarograph is used. In this device the graph is to a much larger scale, and it is possible to obtain readings to within 0.02 in. Hg (0.5 mm Hg).

See also: Air; Altimeter; Gravitation; Pen recorder; Pressure; Vacuum, Vernier gauge.

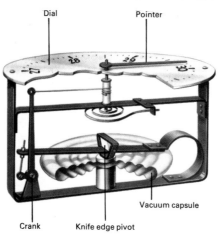

Dial　Pointer

Crank　Knife edge pivot　Vacuum capsule

Far left: An eight-inch Vidie type aneroid barometer made in Hamburg, Germany around 1876. Left: The aneroid barometer consists of two corrugated metal diaphragms enclosing a vacuum. Any change in the air pressure on the outside of this chamber is transmitted mechanically to the pointer on the scale.

Battery

The electric battery or cell produces power by means of a chemical reaction, although there are exceptions such as the nuclear battery. A battery can be either primary or secondary: the primary type is normally regarded as unchargeable whereas a secondary cell or storage battery can be recharged.

There are some indications that batteries may have been used by the Parthians, a tribe in what is now Iran, for electroplating jewellery in the third century BC, but the work which led to modern batteries began with the discovery, in the early nineteenth century by an Italian, Alessandro Volta, that he could cause an electric current to pass through a wire by immersing two different metals in a salt solution.

All batteries, be they primary or secondary types, work as a result of a chemical reaction. This reaction produces an electric current because the atoms of which chemical ELEMENTS (pure substances) are made, are held together by electrical forces when they react to form compounds.

The outer layer of an atom is composed of ELECTRONS, tiny particles each carrying a negative electrical charge. These particles are not all permanently attached to their atoms. In all but a few elements (the rare gases), there are invariably loosely bound electrons that can migrate between atoms during chemical reactions.

When an atom gains an electron, it gains an extra negative charge, and so becomes negatively charged as a whole. When it loses one, on the other hand, it becomes positively charged. Atoms or groups of atoms in this charged state are known as IONS. Positive and negative ions are attracted to each other, and when circumstances allow, will move together and combine to form COMPOUNDS. Ions with similar charges repel each other.

The electrons of the atoms of a metal are very easily detached (this is why metals conduct electricity better than other substances). An electric current consists of a flow of electrons through a metal, hopping from atom to atom.

A simple cell consists of two conductors, *plates* of metal or carbon, dipped into a water-based solution, the *electrolyte*. Pure water cannot be used because it is a very good electrical INSULATOR and would block the flow of current, but when certain chemical substances are dissolved in it, water becomes a conductor. Suitable chemical substances fall into three categories. There are the acids such as sulfuric acid; bases or alkalis such as caustic soda; and salts formed by the interaction of an acid and a base.

Electricity is generated in cells because when any of these chemical substances is dissolved in water its MOLECULES break up and become electrically charged ions. A good example is sulfuric acid, H_2SO_4, the molecules of which consist of two atoms of hydrogen, one of sulfur and four oxygen. When dissolved in water the molecules split into three parts; the two atoms of hydrogen separate and in the process each loses an electron, becoming a positively charged hydrogen ion (represented by the sign H^+). The sulfur atom and the four atoms of oxygen remain together as a sulfate group (SO_4), and acquire the two electrons lost by the hydrogen atoms, thus becoming negatively charged (written SO_4^{--}). These groups can combine with others of opposite charge to form other compounds.

If one plate or *electrode* of zinc and one of either copper or carbon is dipped into a sulfuric acid electrolyte and each is externally connected to a load such as a light bulb, a current will flow through the bulb, lighting it. This is because one of the chemical elements chosen for the electrodes is electrically positive (that is, has a tendency to lose

Below: Early batteries appeared in a wide variety of different shapes and sizes.

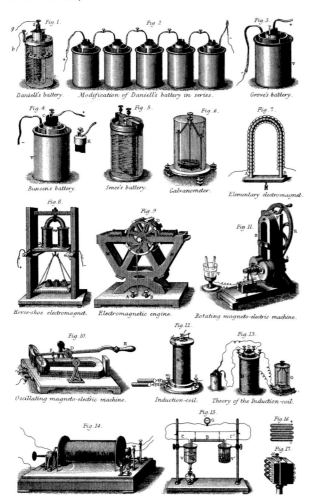

Fig. 1. Fig. 2. Fig. 3.
Daniell's battery. Modification of Daniell's battery in series. Grove's battery.

Fig. 4. Fig. 5. Fig. 6. Fig. 7.
Bunsen's battery. Smee's battery. Galvanometer. Elementary electromagnet.

Fig. 8. Fig. 9. Fig. 11.
Horse-shoe electromagnet. Electromagnetic engine. Rotating magneto-electric machine.

Fig. 10. Fig. 12. Fig. 13.
Oscillating magneto-electric machine. Induction-coil. Theory of the Induction-coil.

Fig. 14. Fig. 15. Fig. 16. Fig. 17.
Ruhmkorff's coil. Thermo-electric circuit. Thermo-pile.

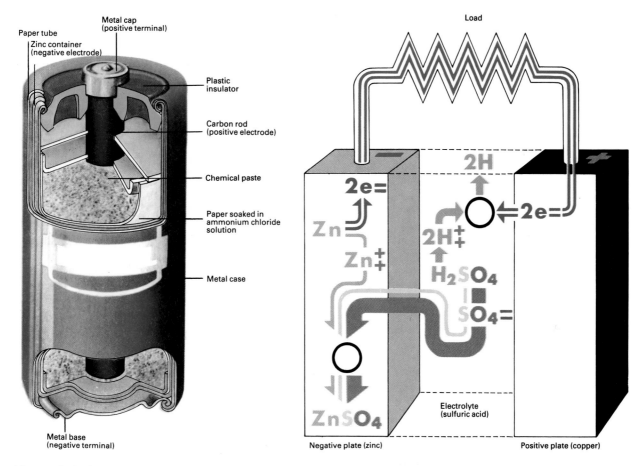

Paper tube

Metal cap
(positive terminal)

Zinc container
(negative electrode)

Plastic
insulator

Carbon rod
(positive electrode)

Chemical paste

Paper soaked in
ammonium chloride
solution

Metal case

Metal base
(negative terminal)

Load

$2e=$

Zn

Zn^+_+

$2H$

$2e=$

$2H^+_+$

H_2SO_4

$SO_4=$

$ZnSO_4$

Electrolyte
(sulfuric acid)

Negative plate (zinc)

Positive plate (copper)

Above: A dry battery cell is not really dry at all –
it is filled with an electrolytic paste comprised of
manganese dioxide and graphite.

Above: In a basic cell the chemical reaction which
produces the current consumes the zinc cathode and
cannot, therefore, be reversed.

electrons and acquire a positive charge) with respect to the other, and when they are electrically connected the chemical equilibrium of the cell is upset and reactions start at both plates. Under these circumstances, the atoms of zinc each give up two electrons which flow through the external circuit and form the current. The positively charged zinc atoms left behind dissolve into the electrolyte and each one combines with one of the negatively charged sulfate ions. The result is a neutral zinc sulfate molecule. The two electrons originally given up by each zinc atom travel around the external circuit and reach the other plate. There they combine with and neutralize the positive charges on two hydrogen atoms from the electrolyte. These two neutral hydrogen atoms then combine to form a molecule of hydrogen gas, and gas bubbles are produced at that plate or electrode.

In theory, the chemical reaction would go on and electric current would continue to flow until all the zinc on the zinc plate (known as the negative electrode or *cathode*) has been used up. But in the simple cell a film of hydrogen bubbles begins to form on the copper or carbon plate (known as the positive electrode or *anode*), and as hydrogen has a much higher electrical resistance than the electrolyte proper, the internal resistance of the cell increases, reducing the current that can flow in the external circuit. At the same time, a voltage (a difference in electrical charge) is produced between the hydrogen and the zinc, and this voltage is in opposition to the main voltage produced between the zinc and the copper or carbon plate, further reducing the available voltage and current.

If the external circuit is disconnected, the hydrogen bubbles will gradually disappear and the cell can be used again, but the same thing will re-occur. In all modern batteries this effect, which is known as *polarization*, is greatly reduced by surrounding the positive electrode with a material known as the *depolarizer*. This works either by reacting with the hydrogen to form water or by taking over from the hydrogen the task of accepting the electrons as they arrive from the external circuit.

The Leclanché cell

The "dry" batteries used in flashlights and so on, which have a depolarizer, are of a type known as Leclanché with modifications to make the liquid electrolyte a semisolid. In its original form the Leclanché cell was entirely "wet" with an electrolyte consisting of a strong solution of ammonium chloride. A zinc plate was used for the negative electrode, and carbon rod packed into a porous pot containing crushed carbon and manganese dioxide (to accept the electrons) formed the positive electrode and its depolarizer. Similar materials are used in a modern dry Leclanché cell. The electrolyte is not, in fact, dry but is made up in the form of a moist paste or jelly.

Additives include mercuric chloride introduced to inhibit what is known as *local action*. This is the name given to the chemical reactions that occur between zinc atoms and carbon and iron atoms which occur as impurities in the zinc plate. It can be overcome by a process known as amalgamation in which the mercury forms an amalgam or alloy with the zinc, preventing it from reacting with its impurities. Other additives include potassium dichromate which inhibits the corrosion of the zinc – an effect that would otherwise reduce the shelf life of the battery, that is, the length of time it can be stored without deterioration.

In the cylindrical Leclanché cell used in flashlights the zinc forms the outer casing and is also the negative electrode. The positive electrode consists of a mixture of graphite (carbon) and manganese dioxide depolarizer around a graphite rod.

Dry cells are supplied singly or in groups of two, three or more to give higher voltages. This is known as a series connection, and the positive electrode of one cell is connected to the negative electrode of the next. High voltage batteries, in which sixty or more individual cells are connected in series, are available but are very heavy and cumbersome. A lighter and more compact construction, where large numbers of cells are to be connected in series, is the flat or layer type. Batteries of this type consist of alternate thin, flat layers of zinc electrolyte and the materials making up the positive electrode and its respective depolarizer.

Other batteries

A disadvantage of Leclanché cells is that the current quickly falls, principally because hydrogen forms more quickly than it can be removed by the depolarizer. For this reason they are best suited to intermittent work. A more constant voltage and current is provided by the mercury cell widely used in hearing aids where almost continuous operation is necessary. In this type of cell, the full name of which is zinc-mercuric oxide, the electrolyte consists of potassium hydroxide. The negative elec-

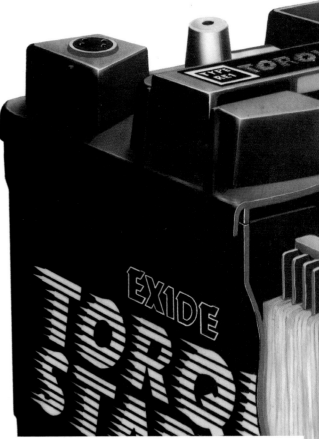

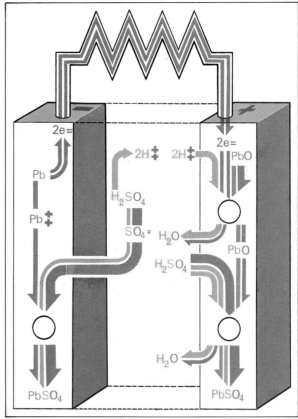

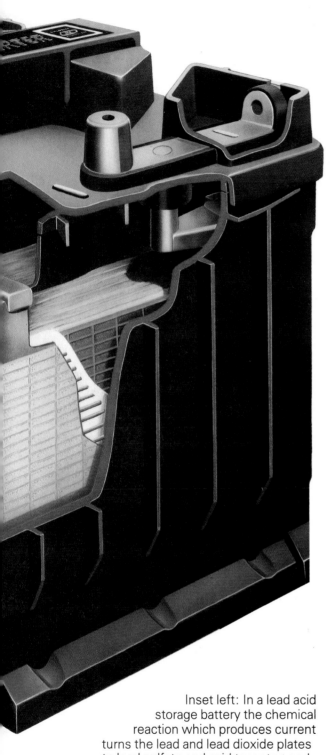

Above: When a battery is recharged, a gas is produced by the chemical reaction. Here a silver zinc unit emits hydrogen bubbles.

Inset left: In a lead acid storage battery the chemical reaction which produces current turns the lead and lead dioxide plates to lead sulfate and acid to water, and passing a current through it in the opposite direction, reverses this process.
Above: Although the chemical operating principle of the lead acid battery has remained unchanged, the comprehensive use of new materials in the last 20 years has increased the ratio of available energy to weight by well over 50 per cent.

trode is zinc, as in the Leclanché cell, but the positive electrode and its depolarizer consist of graphite and mercuric oxide.

A lead-acid battery, as used in a car, does not in practice consist simply of two plates dipped in acid. Lead dioxide is too brittle, and while pure lead is rigid, the lead that is deposited on the negative plate by the charging process builds up as a sort of metal sponge, which is very fragile. Consequently, both plates need some sort of support.

This is normally accomplished by making the plates in the form of grids of an alloy of lead and antimony (which is tougher than pure lead) with the spongy lead or lead dioxide pressed into the grid. There are several grids in each cell of the battery arranged so that positive and negative alternate. They are spaced a short distance apart by separators to make the construction more rigid.

A single *cell*, that is, one set of plates immersed in a single container of acid, produces electricity at the comparatively low voltage of 2V. The electrical system of most modern automobiles runs on 12V; this is provided by linking six cells together in *series*

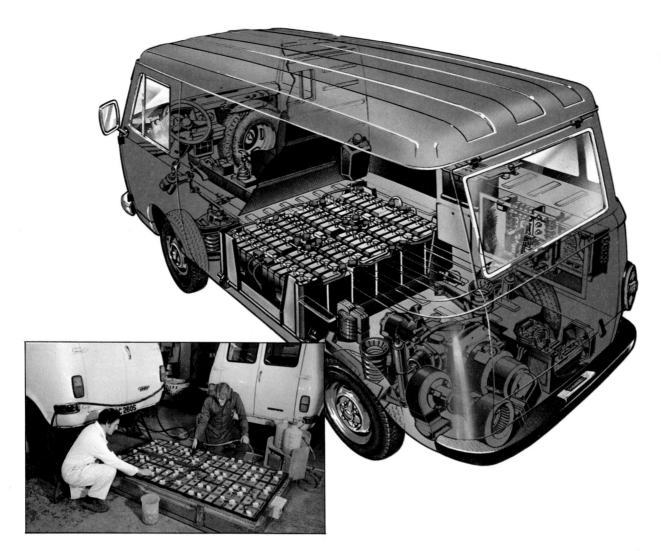

Above: A battery-powered delivery vehicle and a battery pack (inset) being serviced. The greatest breakthrough in electronic vehicle technology will come in the form of new, lighter batteries with greatly increased power output.

(end-to-end) so as to take advantage of their combined voltage. The six cells are completely separate except for linking bars across the top to carry the current from one to another.

A lead-acid battery must not be allowed to remain discharged for a long time. This is because the lead sulfate, which is deposited in *microcrystalline* form (in small crystals), tends to harden into a solid block. Once it has done this it will not take part in any chemical reaction and the plate becomes partly or wholly dead, depending on how much of it is affected. This change is known as *sulfating*.

The state of charge of a battery can easily be discovered by measuring the density of the acid. As the battery discharges so the acid turns to water and the lighter it becomes. Its density is measured with a hydrometer. When the battery is recharged, it becomes warm. Some of the water evaporates, so storage batteries must be topped up occasionally with pure, distilled water.

Other types

The lead-acid battery is a simple and durable device but it is rather heavy. Other, lighter types of battery have been invented. The most important of these are the NiFe (pronounced knife) cell invented by Thomas Edison, and the Nickel Cadmium cell.

The NiFe cell is light and robust, but each cell of a battery only produces 1.2V instead of the 2V of a lead-acid cell. As a result, more cells are needed to produce a given voltage. This, and greater manufacturing cost, make the NiFe system considerably more expensive. It is used in portable radio transmitters because of its lightness. Nickel Cadmium cells are becoming lighter and more powerful, as

Above: Research into power sources for use in space might lead to more powerful batteries.

Above: Automobile manufacturers are among the leaders in the search for efficient batteries.

well as cheaper, and are being developed for use in high-performance electric vehicles.

The main area of research has been to replace the conventional lead-acid battery with a smaller, more efficient unit. This would greatly increase the practicality of electric vehicles, especially for city use where range and speed are less critical factors.

One possibility is the sodium-sulfur battery which could, in theory, achieve an energy density of 2.5 MJ per kg. The sodium-sulfur battery is unusual because it is made from B-alumina which is a form of aluminum oxide. This allows sodium ions to pass freely through at a high temperature, usually around 570° F (300° C). At this temperature the sodium and sulfur are both liquid and are held apart by a solid alumina tube which constitutes the electrolyte. The cells are packed into a thermally insulated stainless steel canister which controls the heat loss. At the present state of development it is possible to get an energy density for such batteries better than 0.5 MJ per kg.

• FACT FILE •

- Battery-operated cars outnumbered cars with gasoline engines in the U.S. at the turn of the century. In 1900 939 gasoline-engined cars were built, compared with 1575 electric cars. In 1899 an electric car had been the first to break the 60 mph (100 km/h) barrier, taking the World Land Speed Record during a record run at Acheres near Paris.

- Acting as a low voltage battery producing direct current, a photo-voltaic (PV) cell produces electricity from light or solar radiation. Already functioning in satellites, private homes, and even in experimental aircraft, PV cells produce electricity when the light reacts with certain semiconductor materials such as silicon, cadmium sulphide and gallium arsenide.

- New plastic materials called electrically conducting polymers, or synmetals, could be used to make batteries that deliver twice the power of conventional lead-acid automobile batteries, while weighing considerably less. Lightweight plastic batteries could be repeatedly charged and discharged without degradation, and molded into any convenient shape.

See also: Atom and molecule; Compound; Electricity; Electric vehicle; Element, chemical.

Packs of power

The form of electric battery known as a fuel cell has existed for less than 25 years. In the beginning great things were expected of it – and indeed some great things have come of it – but overall, its initial promise has not been fulfilled and present applications are few, far between and relatively specialized – largely space flight.

In many ways, a fuel cell is very like any other battery: it produces electric power directly from a chemical reaction between two elements undergoing a form of either oxidation or reduction in the presence of a catalyst and an electrolyte. The fuel cell differs in that the two elements are not an integral part of the cell structure, but are fed in continuously from outside, in the form of liquid or gas. Although this means that a system must be set up to supply the two elements, usually oxygen and hydrogen, at a suitable rate and pressure, and to deal with heat and any residue (commonly water) resulting from the reaction, the main advantage of a fuel cell over an ordinary battery is that as long as such a system remains operative, power generation continues – there is never any need to stop the vehicle and recharge the source of power.

The use of hydrogen and oxygen characterized the first fuel cell ever invented which was devised by an Englishman, Francis Bacon, in 1959. Thereafter, the classic Bacon cell has essentially comprised a three-chambered vessel, the outer chambers of which are connected to supplies either of oxygen or hydrogen, the middle chamber containing an electrolyte, commonly potassium hydroxide solution. The semiporous separating walls constitute the electrodes – the negative anode on the hydrogen side, the positive cathode on the oxygen side. Both hydrogen and oxygen seep slowly through their respective electrodes, adsorbing onto the inner surfaces and thus encountering the electrolyte solution.

So efficient is the generation of electrical energy in this fashion that this type of fuel cell has been successfully used as the primary electric power source for spacecraft, notably for the Apollo Moon missions and for the Space Shuttles.

There are now several other types of fuel cell. One, in order to avoid using fuels as expensive as pure hydrogen and oxygen, makes use of conventional hydrocarbon-compound fuels. Chemical reactions that are inevitably involved mean that the electrolyte used in such circumstances must be both acidic and capable of having the resultant

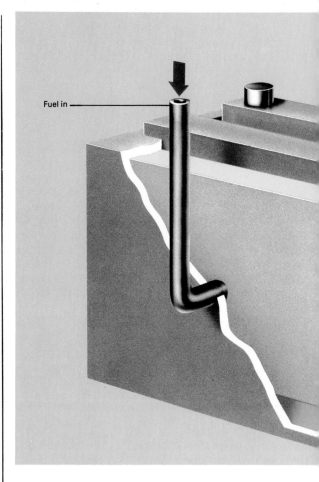

Fuel in

carbon dioxide and water evaporated out with no loss. This means a choice of only two possible electrolytes: sulfuric acid or phosphoric acid. Both have been successfully used – but consequent corrosion factors and the difficulties involved in handling have tended to mar overall cost-effectiveness.

Similar difficulties in finding a suitable electrolyte have bedevilled research into alkaline fuel cells, although a few of these have been put to specialized military use. In attempting further to discover cheaper catalysts, experiments have been carried out to ascertain the effect on electrolytes of higher temperatures: problems of instability and further corrosion have been the unfortunate result. Another type of alkaline fuel cell uses hydrazine (N_2H_2) actually dissolved in the potassium hydroxide electrolyte. Such cells are extremely expensive, and of course the fuel is highly toxic. Nevertheless, a similar system involving methanol (methyl alcohol) is occasionally used to power remote marine buoys and beacons, or unmanned TV booster stations.

Fuel cells have therefore proved their uses. Their

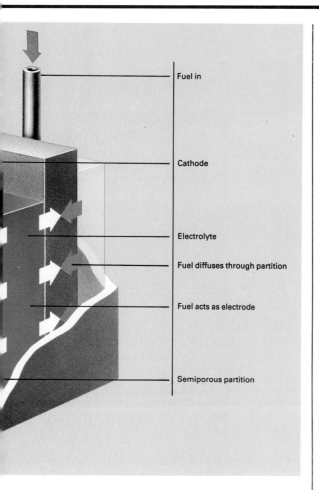

Fuel in

Cathode

Electrolyte

Fuel diffuses through partition

Fuel acts as electrode

Semiporous partition

Above: The Space Shuttle uses hydrogen/ oxygen fuel cells to power its electrical equipment. Enough fuel is carried to run the cells – located beneath the floor of the cargo bay – continuously throughout the duration of an orbital flight. Left: A fuel cell is basically a battery where the anode and cathode are gases and liquids reacting with the electrolyte in the presence of the catalytic partition.

efficiency is almost 100 per cent as long as a supply of the fuels is maintained. It is that very problem of fuel storage and supply which precludes the use of fuel cells to power electrical apparatus in space-flights longer than those to the Moon or orbiting the Earth. Yet the hydrogen-oxygen fuel cell's gaseous fuels are to some extent recyclable – and it is regarded as useful on a space mission to have both oxygen and water available. There are dangers, however: it was the oxygen tank supplying the fuel cell that exploded on Apollo 13, causing near catastrophic disaster.

Some research is looking at the possibility of generating electricity on a national scale. A fuel cell's near-total efficiency compared with an efficiency rate for coal or oil-fired generation remains, however, the only major use for the fuel cell so far.

All the same, there is another use: to monitor the level or lack of oxygen in enclosed atmospheres. Deprived of oxygen, a fuel cell cannot work; given a small amount, the resultant power output can be metered. This perversion of the fuel cell's primary purpose is now quite significant in scientific research in industrial physics and chemistry.

Nevertheless, the fuel cell has not lived up to its early promise. A number of the contributory problems have already been mentioned, but the over-riding one is cost. Although to set up a system of fuel cells for national power generation would be considerably cheaper than building coal- or oil-fired power stations, the relative cheapness of coal and oil far outweighs the expense of the equivalent fuels of the fuel cell – even though the system in operation is not unreasonably expensive in itself. But besides the cost of the fuels, there are also other costs, such as the catalysts. Fuel cells are not suitable, either, for the powering of vehicles: their power-to-weight ratio is prohibitive in this respect. Meanwhile, ordinary batteries have continued to evolve – and, of course, have comparable efficiency for a finite lifetime. General interest in solar and nuclear energy has also increased: both forms are far less efficient in energy conversion but have captured the imagination – and the funding – of the public. The result is that there are very few research units in the world still interested in fuel cells.

Bazooka

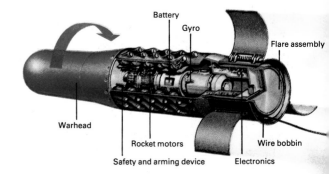

Bazooka has become the generic name for shoulder-launched, man-portable antitank rocket systems after the first such weapon which came into service with the U.S. Army in 1941. The name came from the musical horn used by the American comedian Bob Burns but the weapon itself was an extremely serious addition to the infantryman's capacity to destroy armor. The loaded launcher only weighed 16.75 lbs (7.6 kg) but it could throw a warhead 2100 ft (640 m) to detonate a shaped charge that would penetrate 5 in. (127 mm) of armor.

Rockets had been used for centuries but the bazooka introduced new principles of safety and accuracy that have made it the ancestor of a host of modern battlefield weapons. The rocket was battery fired and there was no recoil because the force of the propellant gases blasting from the rear of the tube equalled the force of the rocket being launched from the muzzle at 265 ft/s (80 m/s). The important thing was that the propellant was fast burning so that it would all be consumed before the rocket left the tube. This meant that there was a dangerous area of blast and flame immediately behind the tube but, in most cases, there was no flashback to injure the firer as the rocket left the tube. Unfortunately, in the original version, cold weather retarded the burning of the propellant which did make the weapon dangerous to use.

Advances in rocket technology have made great differences to the problem of launching without inducing a flashback. In the original bazooka the rocket was not powered once it had left the mouth of the launch tube as its propellant had been completely expended and the rocket itself then became a mere projectile. In order to increase range and shorten the time of flight there was an inevitable demand for an increased thrust. In addition to this shoulder-launched rockets were seen to have a role as antiaircraft weapons so they obviously needed great speed to catch and strike targets travelling at supersonic speed. The answer was found in a two stage rocket round. It is typical for modern shoulder-launched rockets to have an initial eject motor which propels the rocket to a safe distance in front of the firer before the main rocket motor cuts in to take the missile on to its target. The U.S. Army's Stinger missile has a separable booster launcher that takes it more than 40 ft (12 m) from the operator before its main motors fire and take it to supersonic speed to engage aircraft targets. In the case of the Stinger which is a guided missile, change of direction is effected by altering the rocket thrust by blanking off part of one of the two exhaust nozzles. In other guided systems, fins or wings spring from the sides of the rocket after launch and

Above: Short Brothers' Javelin features a Semi-automatic Command-to-line-of-Sight guidance.

these can be manipulated by command to alter flight course.

In addition to this the Stinger is a throwaway round. The original bazooka tube had to be loaded with a rocket and delicately fuzed warhead in an anxious and lengthy operation. A lot of its modern descendants are throwaway and simply have to be clipped to an initiator mechanism for use. Each disposable launch tube contains a single rocket and is delivered to the operator as a certifiable round. In the case of the Stinger each round is clipped to a gripstock which will effect the cycle of prelaunch functions and then the launch itself.

With guided missiles the business of firing has become more complex. The original bazooka was battery initiated but this was found to be unsatisfactory in very low temperatures. Modern dry batteries are more powerful but different systems are also used – the U.S. M47 Dragon antitank weapon uses a gas generator to launch the rocket. Gas generators can also be used to produce the prelaunch function necessary for a guided missile's

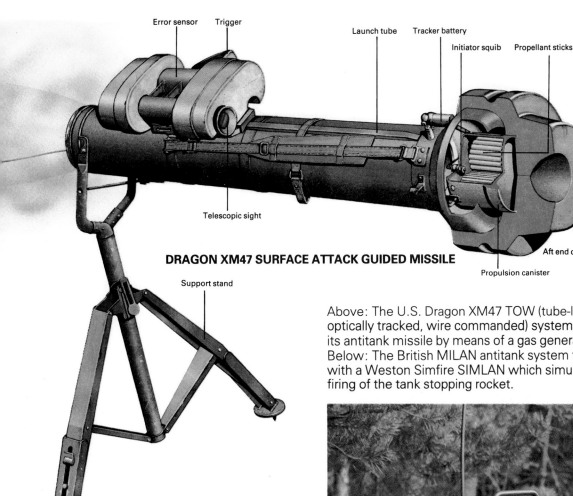

Error sensor   Trigger

Launch tube   Tracker battery

Initiator squib   Propellant sticks

Telescopic sight

Aft end cap

DRAGON XM47 SURFACE ATTACK GUIDED MISSILE

Propulsion canister

Support stand

Above: The U.S. Dragon XM47 TOW (tube-launched, optically tracked, wire commanded) system launches its antitank missile by means of a gas generator. Below: The British MILAN antitank system fitted with a Weston Simfire SIMLAN which simulates the firing of the tank stopping rocket.

accuracy. The first bazooka was a mere rocket-launched projectile but its successors can adjust direction while on a continuously powered flight. For the sake of guidance these missiles rely on navigation systems centered on a gyro which has to be spun up to operating speed before launch. In the U.S. TOW Heavy antitank system the initial spin is imparted to the gyro by a release of gas before the launch of the rocket.

The numbers and variety of small rockets in military use are now very great indeed. The anti-armor weapons can be used very effectively against concrete emplacements and rocky sangars as well as armored vehicles. Besides their High Explosive warheads they can also carry incendiary, smoke or chemical gas warheads. Some types are used as fast moving targets and others are mounted in aircraft. They have also long had a civilian use as distress signals at sea and similar danger areas.

See also: Ballistics; Dynamics; Explosive; Gyroscope; Inertial guidance; Recoilless gun.

Bearing and bushing

A force is always required to slide one object over another in order to overcome the resistance or friction between the two surfaces. FRICTION is usually a hindrance in machines, absorbing power, producing heat, reducing efficiency and promoting wear which limits the life of the machine.

A bearing is a device which will reduce this friction while supporting a load. The moving member can be either rotating, such as the wheel of a bicycle, or it can be a flat surface such as a tool holder sliding along a lathe bed.

Bearings can be classified into three groups: the first being rolling-element bearings; the second, fluid-film bearings; and the third rubbing bearings.

Rolling element bearings

The ancient Egyptians used a type of rolling bearing when they moved the huge stones needed for the pyramids by rolling them along on logs. They realized that such a system meant less work. Modern rolling-element bearings are precision mechanisms but work on the same principle using either balls or cylindrical rollers between two surfaces. As with the use of logs in earlier times, the force required to roll one part over the other is very small compared with the force which would otherwise be required to slide one part over the other.

Rolling-element bearings are used today in automobile wheel hubs and transmissions, electric motors, washing machines, ventilation fans, textile machinery and all types of industrial machines. Such bearings are comparatively friction-free (rolling friction between metals being about one hundredth of the sliding friction). Any energy losses that occur are because of the compression of the metals and the motion of the lubricant.

The most common type of rolling bearing for rotating mechanisms consists of four basic parts: the inner ring or race; the rolling elements (either balls or rollers) of which there are several; a cage to retain and separate the balls or rollers; and an outer race. The inner and outer races and the rolling elements are made in a hard ALLOY steel to give a long life and to prevent permanent indentation of the races at the contact points when under load. The cage is made of soft steel, brass, or plastic resin.

Types of rolling bearings

Ball bearings are normally used to carry radial loads, that is, loads perpendicular or at right angles to the axis of the shaft. Other types are available which will accommodate axial or end thrust loads, while some will carry combined radial and thrust loads. Depending upon the type of bearing, the rolling elements can be cylindrical (log shaped), convex (barrel shaped) or tapered. Taper roller bearings are often used in automobile wheel hubs where the weight of the vehicle has to be supported, and the sideways cornering forces resisted.

Below: The outer race of a roller bearing during manufacture. After forming the upper edge, the barrel-shaped cylinder forms the central groove.

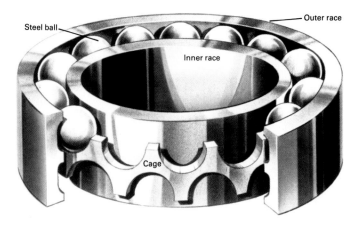

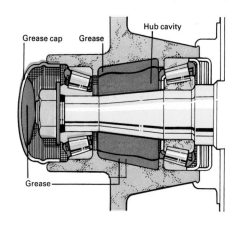

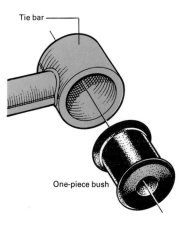

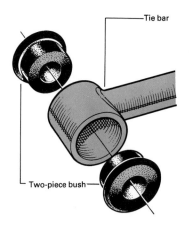

Above left: A sectioned heavy-duty ball journal bearing, designed to support loads perpendicular to the shaft. This type of bearing is not suitable to support an automobile hub, for example, which needs a tapered roller bearing on each side (above) to withstand the sideways forces due to turning corners, as well as the weight of the car. Where the motion is not circular, bushings in single or two-piece units (left) can be used to absorb shock.

Fatigue life

When rolling bearings are subjected to load and rotation, the balls or rollers and the races undergo repeated application of stress at the contact areas, which may ultimately show signs of fatigue failure. Metal fatigue in rolling bearings gives rise to surface pits or craters which cause noisy operation and necessitate replacement. The length of time a bearing will operate until surface pitting begins is known as the *fatigue life*. The principal external factors which affect the fatigue life are the *load* which, for a given size and type of bearing determines the contact stress, and the *rotational speed* which determines how frequently the contact stress is applied.

Because of variations in materials and conditions, the fatigue life prediction is usually based on a rotational life – usually one million revolutions – reached or exceeded by 90 per cent of identical bearings operating at the same load and speed.

Lubrication

Rolling bearings must be lubricated for long life and quiet operation. The majority, including many automobile and household equipment bearings, are partly filled with grease which in some cases lasts the life of the machine. In most industrial applications where heat is developed in the bearings, circulating oil is used as the lubricant and as a means of removing the heat. In communication satellites, which are required to remain in space for 7 to 10 years, lubrication of the ball bearings in gyroscope and solar paddle mechanisms is critical because the grease tends to evaporate and dry up in the vacuum of space. In this and other difficult situations – for example in high temperature applications – greases made from synthetic materials are used.

Fluid-film bearings

In fluid-film bearings the frictional forces are reduced by putting a film of fluid instead of balls or rollers between the two surfaces. The fluid is usually oil, such as in automobile engine bearings, but it can be water (pump bearings) or even air or gas, depending on the application.

The two main types of fluid-film bearing are the *hydrodynamic*, in which the fluid-film pressure is generated by rotation, and the *hydrostatic*, in which the fluid is supplied under pressure from an external source, such as a compressor.

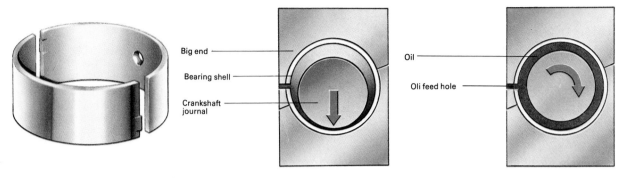

Above left: Shell bearings in halves, used to separate the crankpin from the crankshaft of automobile engines. At rest (above center), the crankpin rests on the bearing (the clearance is exaggerated for clarity), but glides on a film of oil when the engine turns at its normal operating speed (above right).
Left: A ball bearing and cage under seizure test.

The majority of fluid film bearings are hydrodynamic. Here fluid film pressure required to separate the loaded surfaces is generated by the movement or rotation of one part relative to the other. Automobile engine crankshaft bearings operate on this principle and although there is an oil pump, its purpose is only to supply oil to the bearing, and the pressure is not sufficient to support the load. When the engine is stopped, the oil film is squeezed out and the metals touch. Water skiing uses a similar hydrodynamic principle (aquaplaning) where the movement of the skis relative to the water produces a pressure sufficient to support the weight of the skier. If the speed is too low then the skier will sink. Hydrodynamic bearings are used, therefore, in applications where the speed of rotation is high enough to produce a supporting fluid film, such as in automotive engines, steam turbines, alternators for producing electricity, steel rolling mills (though some modern mills use rolling element bearings), and paper making machinery.

Because there is no film separation when the machine is being started and stopped, bearings of this type have to be made in materials which will permit some rubbing contact with the shaft (which is usually of steel) without causing damage. Generally soft bearing materials are preferred, provided their strength is adequate. Soft materials allow dirt to be embedded which would otherwise score the surfaces. Moreover soft metals generate very little heat when rubbing occurs and do not weld or seize when in rubbing contact with a steel shaft. The softest metal bearings for light loads are made from *white metals* (also known as Babbitt metal). These are alloys, mainly of lead and tin. Next in hardness are the copper-lead alloys, and harder still are the bronzes which are basically alloys of copper, tin and lead. Phosphor bronze is the hardest alloy and is used for very highly loaded bearings like diesel engine piston pin bushings. Other metals such as antimony, nickel and aluminum are also used in some of these bearing alloys.

There are many applications of slow-speed bearings such as chemical drum driers, plate shears, dock gates, large blanking presses, and so on, where full film generation is not obtained. In such cases the bearing materials given above are normally used and the system is lubricated with grease.

In some bearing applications where air is used as the separating medium rather than oil or water, the principle of operation is aerodynamic and not hydrodynamic. Self-acting air bearings are being developed for textile spinning machinery where the spinning spindles rotate at very high speeds, say 50,000 revolutions per minute, and where oil lubrication is undesirable because of possible staining of the yarn. Other problems associated with spinning machinery – noise, friction and wear are all minimized by using air bearings. Air bearings of this type are only suitable for high speeds, light loads and in small sizes – up to 1 in. (25 mm) dia.

Hydrostatic bearings

Hydrostatic bearings are not widely used as they require a pumped supply of fluid under pressure to separate the two surfaces. The pressure must be high enough to support the load. The bearing itself is not very different from a hydrodynamic bearing except for the addition of pockets or recesses in the bearing surface into which the fluid is pumped, and as there is never any metallic contact, steel or similar materials can be used throughout. The system, however, is expensive to make, principally because of the need for a high pressure pump and motor with a complicated control system.

Hydrostatic bearings are used where heavy loads have to be supported at very slow speeds or even when stationary, and where under these conditions friction must be kept to a minimum. Some precision machine tools use this type of bearing in the form of flat pads to support the heavy table on which the work piece is carried. A good example of the application of hydrostatic bearings is in large telescopes, such as the famous Hale telescope at Mount Palomar in California. The moving parts weigh 500 tons and are supported on three hydrostatic bearing pads. The whole apparatus is driven by a 1/12 horsepower motor, and in fact could be moved by hand.

Bearings of this type but using air as the pressurized support film are properly called *aerostatic* bearings. Air cushion vehicles work on this principle: air is blown into the underside of the hull at sufficient pressure to support the weight and to lift the hull. One of the first aerostatic bearings was developed for dental drills which rotate at about 500,000 revolutions per minute and are driven by a small air turbine which also supplies air to the bearings. Another example where air (or rather gas) bearings have been used is in some gas-cooled nuclear reactors, where, because of radioactivity and the need to prevent contamination of the circuit with lubricating oil, the gas circulators have been completely sealed, and their bearings continuously pressurized with circuit gas. In this case carbon dioxide is used.

Rubbing bearings

In recent years a great variety of plastic materials have been developed which have proved to be very useful in many bearing applications. The materials include phenolic, epoxy, and cresylic resins which are usually reinforced with cloth, nylon, acetal, and polytetrafluoroethylene (PTFE). PTFE is also used as a coating on nonstick pans.

These materials have the advantage over metal bearings of being able to operate dry – that is unlubricated. This is a valuable property in some applications, for example in the food and pharmaceutical chemicals industries where contamination of the product has to be avoided. Other advantages are their cheapness and ease of machining, or in some cases molding into the required shape.

The life of plastic bearings in dry conditions is limited by wear. Because of this they are generally only suitable for slow speeds with intermittent operation, or light loads. Lubrication of these bearings greatly increases their wear life, and there are today many applications where the performance of lubricated plastic bearings – usually bushings or sleeve bearings – is better than that of lubricated metal bearings.

Examples are the steering linkage bearings in automobiles which are grease lubricated; dock gate bearings, also grease lubricated; central heating pumps and many other water pump bearings which

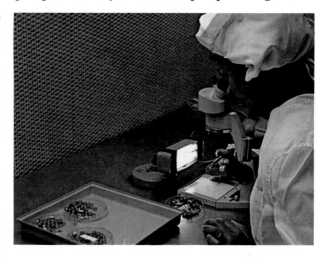

Above: Bearing components are examined to make sure they are free from cracks and blemishes.

are water lubricated; and sliding door wheels and furniture casters, which normally operate dry.

Some rubber bearings are self-lubricating, usually made from sintered metal powders based, mainly, on aluminum, copper, brass, gun-metal or bronze. They are a result of the technology of powder metallurgy, in which very fine powders of metal are precision compressed to the required shape and dimensions. Their porosity depends upon their degree of compactness.

In essence they can be thought of as metal sponges having holes ranging from 1 to 30 thousandths of a millimeter, which can retain up to 30 per cent their volume of oil. Typical applications are as clutch release bearings and main bearings for automobiles and other light-duty applications.

Their main advantage is that they do not depend upon an external oil supply, are cheap to make, and can be installed with relatively little difficulty.

See also: Alloy: Friction; Lubrication; Metal.

Beer and brewing

Beer has been made in various forms for at least six thousand years, and is known to have been made by the Babylonians and ancient Egyptians. In early times, brewing was a cottage craft carried out at the same time as baking, since the initial processes of brewing were then very similar to those of bread making. Primitive types of beer were produced by steeping partly cooked bread crumbs in water and allowing them to ferment. The bread was made from a mixture of crushed barley which had begun to germinate (sprout), and yeast.

By the fourteenth century AD, brewing had developed into a separate trade with its own specialized skills. To a considerable extent this was stimulated, over a period of three centuries or so, by the brewing activities of the monasteries. In medieval times the monks were the main producers of beer, serving not only their own needs but also those of the local people. Brewing was also carried out at home, mostly by the women.

As a trade, brewing then expanded steadily for some five hundred years, notably in Europe and, in the eighteenth century, especially in North America. By the middle of the nineteenth century many thousands of breweries were in operation in the western world. Since then the production of beer has become a major industry and modern breweries are large and complex. World production of beer in 1973 was about 15 times as great as in 1873; in the same period the number of breweries fell ten fold, so on average the 1973 brewery produced 150 times as much beer as its counterpart 100 years before. This very considerable expansion is also well illustrated in brewing technology: the first yeast separator, used commercially in brewing around 1898, could handle 35 cu ft (1 cubic meter) per hour; the capacity of the 1973 version was a significantly larger 7073 cu ft (200 cubic meters) per hour.

Types of beer

Beers can be divided into two main groups: lagers or *bottom fermented* beers, and the *top fermented* British type beers. Some varieties of lager are known by the names of the places in which they were first brewed, such as Pilsener (from Pilsen, in Czechoslovakia) or Dortmunder (from Dortmund in Germany). Most of them are pale in color, carbonated and with a less pronounced hop flavor than British beers; both bottom and top fermentation are used to produce darker, more full bodied beers. Apart from the British Isles, most of the beer brewed throughout the world is of the lager type, generally with an alcohol content of between three and five per cent by weight.

Although an increasing amount of lager is being brewed in Britain, the top fermented ales (beers) and stouts (a type of dark brown beer) are still the most popular. Until the seventeenth century the name ale referred to a drink brewed from malt,

Below left: Well-modified malt being low-temperature dried prior to crushing. Below: Two varieties of beer popular in British pubs.

Far left top: Concentrated hop granules. Far left below: After the malt has been crushed it is mixed with hops and water in the mash tun. Kept at 149° F (65° C), enzymes in the malt degrade the starch in the porridge-like mash into fermentable carbohydrates, polypeptides and valuable amino acids. The wort is then separated off into kettles (left) prior to the boiling operation.

yeast and water, whereas beer was made by the addition of hops during the brewing. Beer was brought to England from Europe in the fifteenth century, and by the early eighteenth it had replaced ale as the main English brew. Although ale as such is no longer made, the name is still applied to any beer which is not a stout or a lager, for example Bitter Ale, Pale Ale, Brown Ale. The alcohol content of ale is usually between 2.5 per cent and 6.5 per cent by weight. Stout, which is brewed with roasted malt and often a high percentage of hops, has a strong, rich flavor. It is very dark, often black in color, containing up to 5.5 per cent of alcohol. Porter was a dark beer of the eighteenth and nineteenth centuries, full bodied but milder than stout.

The brewing process

The raw materials used in brewing have a major influence on the type and quality of the beer produced. In theory, beer can be made by fermenting any cereal, or other source of starch such as potatoes, in water. In practice, barley is the most widely used cereal. Other cereals are used as additives to the main barley *mash* to reduce costs, and sometimes to produce a desired flavor. The main additives are rice, corn, tapioca, soyabean meal, unmalted barley, and various sugars.

The initial brewing operation is to make a sugary liquid mixture from barley, water and hops which is known as *wort*. Barley cannot be used, however, until it has been malted, a process not usually carried out at the brewery itself but at plants known as *maltings*. The malting of barley involves germinating it under controlled conditions to produce natural substances called ENZYMES, which act as CATALYSTS in various chemical reactions vital to brewing. Commercially-produced enzymes from different sources now make it possible to produce wort from unmalted barley but the use of malted barley is still preferred.

To soften the barley and promote its germination, it is soaked in water at 55° to 60° F (13° to 16° C) for between 48 and 72 hours, depending on the type of grain used. After soaking, the barley is put into large drums or boxes, and moist air is blown through it for 7 to 11 days to encourage germination. It is then dried in a kiln until its moisture content is down to 1.5 per cent to 2 per cent. The rootlets which have grown during germination drop off and are used as animal food. The barley is now known as *malt*, and contains enzymes.

At the brewery the malt is crushed and made into a mash with water and the additives. Mashing sets the enzyme process in operation and brings out the carbohydrates, such as starch and sugar, from the malt. Insoluble material such as protein is made soluble by the action of enzymes, which also convert the malt starch into maltose sugar; the amount of maltose produced determines the alcohol content of the beer. The mashing operation must be very carefully controlled so that all the physical and chemical processes and enzyme reactions are coordinated to

produce precisely the type and quality of wort, and therefore beer, which is required. The mashing process for lager beer is different to that for the British top fermented beers.

Infusion mashing

The mashing for British beers is known as infusion mashing. It is carried out in large insulated tanks called *tuns*, which are generally heated by steam. The consistency of the mash is important, so the tuns are often fitted with mechanical agitators such as *rakes*. Precise temperature control is vital, since a deviation of only a few degrees can produce a totally different type of wort from that required.

Once the warm mash has reached the point where starch conversion (to maltose sugar) is complete, the temperature is raised to about 167° F (75° C) for a short time. This operation, known as "mashing off", is carried out to inactivate the enzymes, most of which stop working at this temperature. The mash is then allowed to stand for 30 minutes, to allow the insoluble grain husks to settle out. The husks form a layer on the false bottom inside the run and act as a filter. The liquid wort is run through until it becomes clear; the *spent* or used grains are washed, *sparged*, with sprays of hot water to ensure that all the soluble matter passes through the false bottom of the mash tun into a receiving vessel.

Decoction mashing

The malted barley used in lagers is not germinated for as long as that used in British beers, and so it needs to be more finely mashed. The mashing is done in stages: a preliminary mash at 100° F (37° C), followed by subsequent mashes at 122° F (50° C), 149° F (65° C) and 168° F (75° C); or the quick mash-

Above left: A brewery packing hall where many beers are chilled and pasteurized. Above: Refrigeration is an essential part of the preserving of the flavor of beers which are not pasteurized.

ing system used in the U.S. with two mashes at 149° F (65° C) and 172° F (78° C). The temperature is raised to the various temperature stages by removing part of the mash, heating it to boiling and returning it to the main mash.

Boiling

After mashing, the wort and sparge water are transferred to a large copper vessel known as a brewing kettle, and boiled vigorously with hops or hop extracts (which are sometimes added progressively), for at least two hours. This operation does several things: it sterilizes the wort and reduces its bulk by evaporation of the water; it draws out the full bitter flavor of the hops and helps precipitate any unwanted protein left in the wort; and it ensures that if any enzymes have survived the "mashing off" operation they are now made completely inactive, preventing spoilage of beer in cask or bottle by further reactions.

After boiling, the wort is discharged through a filter bed made from spent hops, and then cooled, usually by heat exchangers, and aerated, which helps fermentation later on.

Fermentation

When the wort is at the optimum temperature for starting fermentation the yeast is added. Yeasts are microscopic organisms related to fungi, and there are thousands of different species. There are many strains of the brewer's yeast (*Saccharomyces cerevisiae*), but they can all be placed into one of two groups: they either rise to the surface or sink to the bottom during fermentation, thus giving top fermented or bottom fermented beers. The particular temperature chosen depends on the quality and strength of the beer, and as yeast is a form of plant the fermenting temperature is also varied at different times of the year. Weaker beers require higher temperatures than stronger beers. The action of the yeast on the wort is extremely complex, producing alcohol and carbon dioxide as the principal products, and many other substances such as acids, esters and glycerin, all of which affect the final flavor and aroma of the beer.

For bottom fermented beers the yeast is added at a temperature of 43° to 50° F (6° to 10° C), and fermentation takes about eight days, after which the *green* beer is put into storage tanks for up to three months (the name *lager* comes from the German word for storage). The lager is stored at 32° F (0° C), and a secondary fermentation occurs which clears the beer and improves the flavor.

British beers begin fermentation at about 60° F (15° C), and during the process the temperature increases to about 70° F (21° C). The fermentation takes five to seven days, followed by a low temperature maturation period, perhaps three weeks.

Whichever process is used, the yeast layers are separated off and may be used in subsequent brews. Fermentation produces more yeast than can be used in this way, and the surplus is used for animal feeds and yeast extract manufacture. The beer may be given a very fine final filtration in order to *polish* it,

that is, to give it more clarity and lightness before it is put into the barrels, bottles or cans. Some ales are subjected to a secondary fermentation process in the barrels in which they are sold, but this is now comparatively rare, since most beer in bulk is now supplied under pressure in aluminum or stainless steel kegs rather than the traditional wood.

The brewing process yields several useful waste products. Animal feedstuffs are made from the dried rootlets and spent grains of the malted barley, and from the yeast residues, which are also used in human foods, pharmaceuticals, and vitamin concentrates (yeast is a rich source of B-group vitamins). Spent hops can be used as fertilizers, but hops as such are gradually being superseded in brewing by hop extract in powder or pellet form, which leaves no major residues. The main constituents of the beer itself are: carbohydrates (5 per cent); protein (0.6 per cent); small amounts of riboflavin, niacin, and thiamine which are forms of vitamin B; traces of calcium and phosphorous; from 2 per cent to 6.5 per cent alcohol; and up to 90 per cent water. One pint (0.56 l) contains about 280 calories.

Modern trends

Apart from the sheer size of production, the trend in the second half of the twentieth century is towards much larger, often international, brewery groups, and more widespread exporting of beer. Emphasis has been placed on speeding up the brewing process.

See also: Alcohol; Enzyme; Fermentation.

Below: Chemical analysis of beer flavor compounds has identified only 150 of the 400 recognizable constituent components.
Below right: The control room of a computerized brewery.

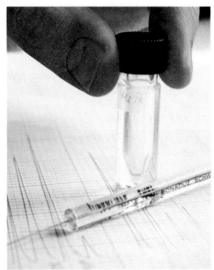

Bell

Bells have been made since prehistoric times. In China heavy bells are said to have been in use since the third century BC. Eastern bells are basically cylinders closed at the top and with increased wall thickness at the open end: they are struck on the outside near the middle.

In Europe bells have changed little in general appearance throughout the Christian era, although the early bells were slightly more conical than those of the present day. Some European churches still use bells cast in the thirteenth century, and some date even earlier.

When a bell is struck the metal is set into vibration and this causes a movement of the air which the listener hears as the characteristic bell sound. The vibration, and therefore the sound, is very complex, over 60 different frequencies being present just after the impact. Most of these fade rapidly so that the note soon contains only ten or so components or *partials*; of these, five, spanning two octaves, predominate and can easily be distinguished by anyone with a musical ear. The nominal – the note which is heard on the impact of the clapper, and the hum note – which swells up afterwards – are the most evident to the unpractised ear; the others being the minor third, the fifth, and the fundamental which is an octave above the hum note, and an octave below the nominal.

Each partial is produced by a different pattern of vibrations over the bell, normally heard all at once.

For each pattern there are certain *nodal* lines. These occur where the metal does not vibrate at all, and they divide the bell into zones of vibration.

Because a bell is never perfectly symmetrical each partial usually occurs not as a single frequency, but as a close pair of frequencies which combine in the listener's ear to give a surging effect known as *beating*. For example, a partial may actually consist of two components, 1000 Hz and 1004 Hz, but it will be heard as a single note at a frequency of 1002 Hz swelling and fading four times every second. Beating can be minimized by careful tuning and selection of the point where the clapper strikes but it can never be completely eliminated; it is therefore another of the characteristic features of the bell sound, particularly noticeable with small, light types of bell.

Bells are cast in bronze (77 per cent copper, 23 per cent tin is typical) because this is a very tough ALLOY – it was used for old fashioned cannon and Roman swords – and does not rust. The molten bell metal is poured into a mold consisting of an inner *core* and outer *cope* which together fix the shape of the bell. The outer surface of the bell usually carries an inscription, cast in raised letters. These are stamped into the *loam*, the material which lines the cope before casting. The loam is a mixture of clay and traditional additives such as chopped hay and horse droppings. These burn when the molten metal is poured in, providing ventilation holes to help the cooling and to prevent stress points from developing in the finished casting.

Old bells had an arrangement of loops cast on the

Below: Big Ben, the bell in the clock tower of Britain's Houses of Parliament was first cast in 1856. Right: The tuning of a bell's various harmonics depends from where the metal is removed.

Above: Molten metal at 2102° F (1150° C) is poured into the space between the core and cope.
Right: Metal is trimmed from the bell on a vertical lathe until the tuning is correct.

top by which they were fixed to their supporting wooden beams with chains. These days, bells are usually made with flat tops which are drilled to take mounting bolts and the support for the clapper. This technique was first used in the nineteenth century, when metal drilling became sufficiently easy.

The general shape of the bell is dictated by experience, but in order to obtain the exact frequencies required the bell is cast a little thicker than the final value. This gives a slightly higher set of frequencies which are decreased in a controlled manner by turning the inside of the bell on a lathe.

Bells in a church belfry are mounted in a frame and have a freely hanging clapper. They are rung by pulling a rope which swings them through about 390°, each stroke starting in an almost vertical position with the open end facing towards the sky. This system is used only when the British art of change-ringing is being practised.

Electric bell

The electric bell found in many houses is made to ring by a very simple device that makes a clapper vibrate against a bell or gong.

The mechanism consists of the bell itself, the clapper that strikes it, which is mounted on a spring, an electromagnet (most bells have one consisting of two coils) and a simple adjustable electrical contact.

When the bell-push is pressed, electricity flows through the contact into the electromagnet. This attracts the iron arm of the clapper, which moves out on its spring and strikes the bell. As it does this, however, it swings away from and breaks the electrical contact, stopping the flow of current through the electromagnet. With the magnetism gone, the arm is pulled back by the spring. When the arm falls back, it touches the contact again, restarting the flow of current to the electromagnet so that the arm moves out again and hits the bell – the cycle repeating itself. The speed of vibration, and to a certain extent the loudness of the bell, can be increased by reducing the distance that the clapper must travel. This is done by adjusting the contacts.

Electric buzzers work on the same principle, but the clapper hits the outer casing of the buzzer instead of a bell, producing a dry sound.

Chimes

The two-tone chimes that some houses have instead of bells are worked in a different way. There is an electromagnet that pulls a clapper over, but no contacts. Instead, the end of the arm has a flexible joint. When the bell-push is pressed current flows through the electromagnet causing the flexible end to swing across and hit the first chime. When the bell-push is released and its arm falls back, the flexible end swings back farther than the arm and hits the other chime. It comes to rest roughly halfway between the chimes ready for next time.

Some sets of chimes have a second bell-push for

Below: An electric door chime works when the steel plunger is flung against the first tone bar by the electromagnet and then against the second tone bar by the reaction of the spring.

the back door connected to the electrical circuit through an electrical resistance. Current to the electromagnet is consequently weaker and the magnetic field produced pulls the arm with less force. If the arm is set off-center between the chimes, it will only hit one of them, thus making it clear whether the caller is at the front door or the back. More complicated chimes with three or more notes are rung by electric motors turning a striker that rings them in order.

Alarms

Some fire and burglar alarm bells on the outside of shops and offices use electric motors rather than electromagnets. Attached to the motor shaft is an arm with a jointed hammer end. The spin causes the hammer to fly outward, striking the bell, but the joint allows the hammer to bend back after striking so that it can pass the bell.

Amplified bells playing through loudspeakers are still found on ambulances and police cars in some countries although solid state electronic noise generators are almost universal.

See also: Alloy: Brass; Electromagnetism; Musical scale; Sound; Transducer.

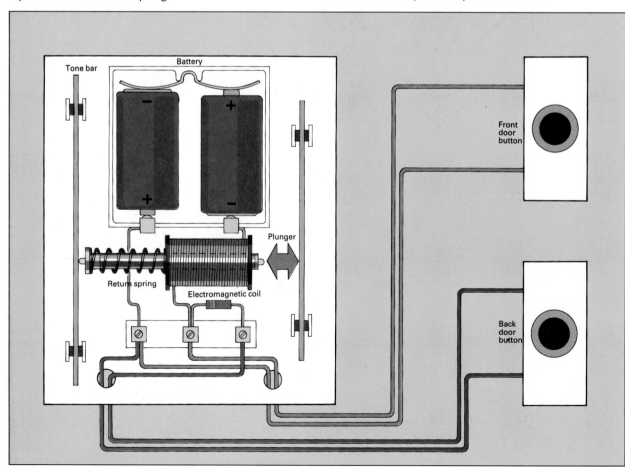

Bicycle

A bicycle is a pedal driven human-powered vehicle with two wheels placed one in front of the other. The name derives from the latin *bi* meaning two and the greek *kyklos* meaning circle or wheel. Similarly, one and three wheeled vehicles are called unicycles and tricycles. Bicycles designed for two pedalers are called tandems.

Cyclists can travel three or four times faster than pedestrians, and they consume less energy in traveling a given distance than any other moving animal or machine. Pound for pound, the cyclist has an energy consumption of approx. $0.15 \, \text{cal} \, \text{g}^{-1} \, \text{km}^{-1}$, compared with figures of 0.4 and 0.6 for salmon and jet planes respectively.

This efficiency derives from the fact that the bicycle is propelled by the thigh muscles, the most powerful in the body, operating in a smooth rotary action at a speed of 60–80 rpm, thus making an extremely efficient use of human power output. The first successful human powered flight across the English Channel was achieved by this method, the rider using no more than a quarter of a horsepower (0.18 kW) for almost three hours. Transmission losses in the gears and roller bush chain of a bicycle are low (1.5 and 5 per cent respectively) and narrow pneumatic tires and light but strong spoked wheels minimize rolling resistance. For comparison, the energy consumption of a cyclist is equivalent to that of a car that could travel 1250 miles on one gallon of gasoline (530 km/l).

Development

A sketch on the back of a sheet of drawings by Leonardo da Vinci (c. 1490) is the earliest known description of a bicycle, although there is no evidence that the machine was ever constructed. A two wheeled hobby horse, the Draisienne, patented by Karl von Drais in 1817, had a wooden frame, spoked wooden wheels with metal tires, a saddle and steerable front wheel.

The first bicycle that could be propelled without the rider's feet touching the ground was a lever-driven model produced by the Scotsman Kirkpatrick Macmillan in or around 1839. The Macmillan machine, which had treadles mounted near the front fork connected to cranks attached to the rear axle, was copied and produced commercially by Thomas McCall, but the idea was not patented, and its influence on the development of later models was quite minimal.

The bicycle was reinvented by Phillipp Fischer of Obendorf in the early 1850s and by another German, Karl Kech in 1862. The first truly commercial

Above: Professional racing cyclists on the grueling Tour de France on cycles trimmed to the limit for lightness and strength. Despite the weight advantage and a choice of ten gear ratios, the riders are severely tested on the mountainous route. Structurally, their racing models are not far removed from early designs, such as the Singer Special Safety (right) made in 1896, which had a diamond-shaped frame.

Above: In India, the Oxtrike or Oxfam three-wheeler is an important commercial vehicle.

Above: In Peking, rush-hour traffic consists not of automobiles but of bicycles.

machine was produced by Pierre and Ernest Michaux in 1861. They fitted cranks and pedals directly onto the front wheel of a steerable veloci-pede (hobby horse).

In 1867 the Boneshaker appeared. This had two wheels and pedals on short cranks fitted to the front wheel. In the 1870s the Ordinary took development a step further. It had a big front wheel measuring 54 in. (137 cm) in diameter for the average man of five foot eight inches, but some had wheels of 60 in. (152 cm) diameter for really tall riders. By comparison, the back wheel was quite small and the machines became known as Penny-Farthings, after the British coins.

James Starley of Coventry invented the Tricycle in 1882. This was the first chain-driven cycle. In 1885 the Rover Safety set a new trend in design and from it developed the Humber bicycle featuring the *diamond* frame, a design which has lasted close on 100 years.

It was popular because its two wheels of equal size and gearing could suit any rider. People could mount and dismount in safety.

Until then tires had been made of solid rubber. In 1888 John Boyd Dunlop's reinvention of the pneumatic tire ended the boneshaking era.

Cycle frame design remained largely unchanged for many years, except for the Dursley-Pedersen in the 1890s. The frame was made of small-diameter tubes in a triangular design, and instead of a leather saddle, a hammock type saddle was strung between handlbars and rear frame tube.

Despite being hailed as the most comfortable bicycle, the Dursley-Pedersen found favor only amongst enthusiasts. It was the diamond frame which was developed and nothing changed for 60 years, except to modify it and improve accessories.

Other developments include the Cross frame, first developed in 1886, which reappeared as the small-wheeled Moulton in 1962. This frame has a main tube running straight from the headset to the back wheel axle, crossed by a second tube in the vertical axis carrying the saddle at the top and the bottom bracket axle at the bottom. In the Moulton this design is reinforced by triangulation around the crossing point.

Transmission systems
The roller bush chain is still used in almost all bicycles, but experiments continue with belt and shaft transmission. The gear sprockets at the bottom bracket and rear wheel axles are connected by an endless chain, and the cycle is propelled by pedals attached to the front sprocket.

In the simplest form, fixed wheel drive, the rear gear sprocket is attached directly to the rear wheel, with no freewheel. Only one gear ratio can be used at a time, the cranks cannot be turned independently of the rear wheel. The fixed wheel bicycle can be braked by the rider resisting the motion of the pedals. Although lighter and more efficient than other systems, this method of transmission is used mainly on track racing bicycles, as the single gear and the necessity to strap the feet firmly to the pedals makes it impractical for general use.

Hub gears are available in 2-, 3-, 4-, and 5-speed

versions. The gear is built inside an enlarged rear hub, and controlled either by a cable or cables passed through the hollow axle or by a back pedalling action. In a standard Sturmey Archer hub gear, the ratios are 4/3, 1/1 and 3/4 of direct drive. Brakes and dynamoes can also be incorporated into hubs in various combinations.

Derailleur gears are named for the method of changing, in which an assembly fixed to the bicycle frame is used to derail the chain from one gear sprocket to another. Five, six, seven or eight sprockets are arranged in order of size on the rear axle, and one, two or three on the crank axle. Both front and rear derailleurs are controlled by cables which pull the arm containing the chain inwards against spring tension. The rear derailleur also acts as a jockey pulley to maintain tension in the chain, taking up the slack that is necessary to accommodate sprockets of various sizes.

Even with derailleur gears, the range of available ratios is limited, and various continuous or automatic gears have been developed. Recent examples include the Biocam, a 50-ratio drive system incorporating double cam shaped chainwheels mounted 180° out of phase. A nonendless chain is driven by the reciprocating motion of these cams, and the effective gear ratio is varied during the power stroke to parallel the muscle action of the rider.

The Deal Drive has a spring loaded variable diameter front chainwheel which is opened or closed to the effective size by the pressure exerted on the chain. An intermittent locking system allows the gear to change only when the chainwheel teeth are free from the chain.

Brakes

Some heavyweight roadsters still have brakes consisting of a plunger rod mounted on the front forks which bears directly down on to the tire tread surface. The more efficient rim brakes pinch the metal rim of the wheel from both sides with equal pressure. Controlled by rods or cables, such brakes are used on almost all lightweight models. The force to close the arms of the brakes is applied either from one side (sidepull), from directly above the wheel (centerpull), or from both sides using brake arms mounted directly onto the forks, thus providing extra leverage (cantilever).

The composition of the brake blocks that come in contact with the rim has a marked effect on braking performance, particularly on wet steel rims. Chrome leather blocks work well on steel, and synthetic materials have been developed to improve braking on alloy rims.

Right: The British Bluebell is a streamlined semi-recumbent. Built exclusively for HPV speed attempts, it has reached speeds of over 50 mph (82 km/h).

Hub brakes, controlled either by back pedaling or by hand lever, are used on heavy roadsters and tandems. Disc brakes can also be used in some cases, and hydraulic control systems have been produced for bicycle brakes.

Tires and wheels

The development of the pneumatic tire greatly improved the comfort and performance of the bicycle, but it also introduced the problem of punctures. Impenetrable tire casings, tough layers inserted between tire and inner tube, liquid sealants inside the tube and even solid plastic tires and solid inner tubes have been produced in an

attempt to overcome this problem, but none are as good as the pneumatic tire.

The *wire-on* tire has an inflatable inner tube and a sturdy outer case with patterned tread surface, held on by a wire bead that fits inside the rim of the wheel. Lightweight racing bicycles have one-piece tubular tires with a light airproof inner membrane.

As with many parts of the bicycle, steel rims and wheel hubs are cheaper but heavier than aluminum alloy components. All-plastic wheels and plastic rims have been developed, although their main use has been in BMX and childrens' bicycles. The strength and characteristics of the wheel are affected by the spoking pattern, and many variants are used. Most bicycles use ball bearings, but roller bearings are produced for specialist use, and cheaper bicycles have nylon bearings.

Frames

The design and composition of the frame is the major factor affecting the performance of the bicycle. The cheapest frames are made from low carbon mild steel which is rolled and welded into seamed tubes. Seamless alloy steel tubing containing various

Below: Racing bicycles attempt to reduce drag to a minimum with aerodynamically designed frame tubes, components and concealed cables.

additives is used to produce lighter and more responsive frames. The best quality frames are made from heat treated manganese/molybdenum steel, double butted so that the walls are thicker at the ends than in the center of the tubes to reduce weight without affecting performance. Cheap frames are welded, but lugged and brazed joints are used in most medium and high quality frames. The new inexpensive high manganese chrome molybdenum steels can be machine brazed easily because of their higher heat tolerance, but top quality frames are hand brazed, some with silver.

Bicycle frames can also be produced in welded or glued aluminum tubing, and some frames and components have been produced in titanium. The all-plastic bicycle has reappeared every ten years or so, but the major use for plastic materials is likely to be for components such as mudguards.

Frames vary from the long wheelbase and heavily raked forks of the roadster to the tight angles and almost straight forks of the racing model. Roadsters are intended for relatively slow but comfortable travelling, and they have straight handlebars and an upright riding position. Bicycles for faster riding or touring over long distances are stiffer but more responsive, with dropped handlebars to allow the rider to crouch and minimize air resistance.

The only major departure from the diamond

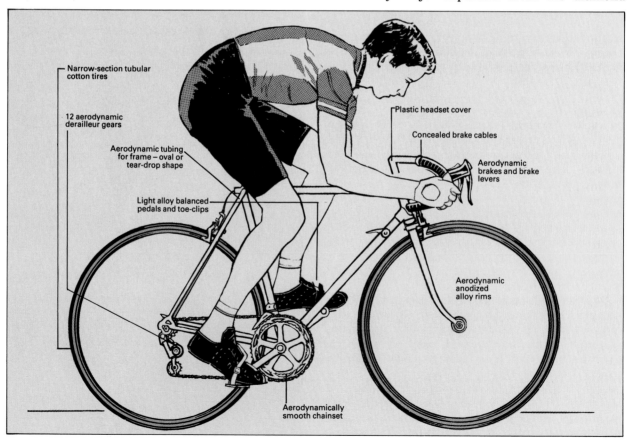

Narrow-section tubular cotton tires

12 aerodynamic derailleur gears

Aerodynamic tubing for frame – oval or tear-drop shape

Light alloy balanced pedals and toe-clips

Plastic headset cover

Concealed brake cables

Aerodynamic brakes and brake levers

Aerodynamic anodized alloy rims

Aerodynamically smooth chainset

Above: The streamlining effect of a plastic windshield more than compensates for the weight.

Above: Powered by five riders, the New Wave Human-powered Vehicle attempts a speed record.

frame during this century is the Moulton, a small wheeled bicycle with a Cross type frame and suspension front and rear. The Moulton combined the riding quality of a full sized bicycle with compact size and suitability for a wider range of riders. Since the Moulton was introduced in 1962 a sizeable share of the market has been taken up by mass-produced small wheel bicycles, but most of these lack the riding qualities of the original.

Many ingenious designs for lightweight folding bicycles have been produced, notably the Bickerton which has an aluminum box section frame, many aluminum components and folds down to a tiny, portable package, weighing approximately 22 lb (10 kg).

Another recent departure is the BMX bicycle for children, which has 20 in. (50.8 cm) wheels, straight forks and a rugged frame intended for rough fast riding and various stunts. The adult cruiser bicycle (Mountain bike) has wide straight handlebars, broad high pressure tires, a responsive frame and high quality gears and brakes. It is intended for both on- and off-road leisure use.

The recumbent human powered vehicle, with either two or three wheels, combines greater use of the riders' power with a more efficient aerodynamic profile. The rider lies prone or supine on the vehicle, pedalling with the back braced against the seat. When enclosed in a light plastic shell, human powered bicycles can travel at up to 50 mph (80 kph) on the flat. With battery motor assist such vehicles could achieve acceleration rates and cruising speeds comparable with those of automobiles.

See also: Aerodynamics; Chain-drive; Friction; Lubrication; Freewheel, bicycle; Road safety.

• FACT FILE •

- Before World War I, the British Army instituted bicycle battalions. A special folding bicycle was developed, and combat techniques from an army manual of the time include instructions on how to deal with cavalry by turning the bicycles upside down, and spinning the wheels to frighten the horses.

- An experimental four-seater tandem developed at the University of Queensland, Australia, also incorporated a rider-shading canopy which was equipped with 440 photovoltaic cells. The PV cells delivered power to a half-horse-power auxiliary electric motor over the rear wheel. In a 1150 mile test run, the solar cells contributed an estimated 25 per cent increase in speed.

- At the 1984 Olympics in Los Angeles, the winning U.S. bicycle track team rode revolutionary new machines with very thin, solid metal wheels. They also wore tear-drop-shaped aerodynamic helmets, and it was later revealed that they had used blood-doping to improve their performance. This is a process involving the transfusion of previously removed, highly oxygenated blood back into the body of an athlete prior to an event.

The low rider

A cyclist is more energy-efficient than any other machine or animal. A compromise between engineering and human demands, the traditional bicycle effectively balances lightness, strength, efficiency and economy. With this characteristic, it is not surprising that bicycle design and materials changed very little for nearly a hundred years.

Recently, however, the incorporation of aerodynamic theory and modern materials has dramatically changed the appearance and performance of some bicycles, producing such oddities as low-slung human-powered vehicles, filament-wound reinforced plastic bicycles and machines with automatic transmission.

Traditional bicycles – with large tires, sprung saddle, and sit-up riding posture – are heavy, and so much of the cyclist's energy output is absorbed by rolling resistance (of the tires on the road). Riding in an erect posture means that up to half of the rider's energy is used to combat wind resistance.

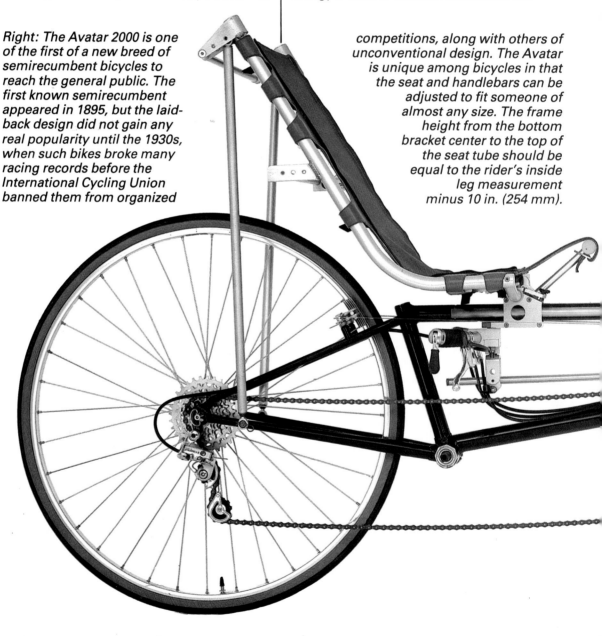

Right: The Avatar 2000 is one of the first of a new breed of semirecumbent bicycles to reach the general public. The first known semirecumbent appeared in 1895, but the laid-back design did not gain any real popularity until the 1930s, when such bikes broke many racing records before the International Cycling Union banned them from organized competitions, along with others of unconventional design. The Avatar is unique among bicycles in that the seat and handlebars can be adjusted to fit someone of almost any size. The frame height from the bottom bracket center to the top of the seat tube should be equal to the rider's inside leg measurement minus 10 in. (254 mm).

Much of the power output of a cyclist is absorbed by these two factors, and as speed increases, so too does the power needed to overcome them. The power needed to overcome rolling resistance is directly proportional to speed – so that at twice the speed, it is twice as great. But the power needed to combat wind resistance is proportional to the cube of the speed – so that at twice the speed, it is *eight* times as great. At low speeds rolling resistance is the greatest hindrance to efficiency. At high speeds, on the other hand, the reduction of wind resistance is of prime importance.

In an attempt to maximize efficiency, a new breed of barely recognizable bicycle has recently emerged – the recumbent.

Constructed close to the ground with riders on their backs or stomachs, often within an aerodynamic shell, recumbents are capable of speeds of more than 60 mph (100 km/h). The laid-back riding position offers greater leverage, despite the drawback that the arms and shoulders cannot contribute to pedaling pressure as they can on a conventional bicycle.

The low center of gravity, long wheelbase and preponderance of weight to the rear of the machine all contribute to the recumbent's stability, excellent cornering ability at speed, and exceedingly good braking capacity. Some think that the recumbent is safer than the conventional bicycle since, in the event of a collision, the rider would be less likely to fall head first – and there isn't so far to fall anyway. Others disagree – the bike's lack of height might well make a collision more likely, since it makes it difficult to see in traffic.

A few semirecumbents (not *totally* supine) were, in fact, manufactured in the 1920s and 1930s. Known as *velocars* in France and horizontal bicycles in Britain, they broke many racing records before being banned for their non-conventional design. Only in the 1970s did recumbents reappear in cycle design competitions introduced by the International Human Powered Vehicle Association.

One of the first semirecumbents produced for the general public, the American *Avatar 2000*, is a two-wheeler without windshield or shell. Its unique design includes handlebars under the saddle, chainwheel and pedals out in front of the machine, and a rear wheel much larger than the front one – 26 in. vs 16 in. (68.6 cm vs 40.6 cm). Its frame looks like a conventional triangulated form that has been squashed and then stretched horizontally.

The handlebars and seat move along stainless steel tracks, making the frame adjustable to fit just about any size. The Avatar's seat webbing and elastic tension straps distribute the impact of uneven surfaces, making the ride unusually comfortable without the soft wallowing associated with true sprung or rubber shock absorber suspension.

Binary

Binary is a system of counting based on the number two. Normally we count using a base ten and the digits 0 to 9. Binary is much simpler – it uses only the digits 0 and 1.

When we write down a number we mean that the far right digit represents units, the next left tens, the next left hundreds (ten times tens), the next left thousands (ten times ten times tens), and so on.

(i) For example:
$$9533 = 9 \times (10 \times 10 \times 10)$$
$$+ 5 \times (10 \times 10)$$
$$+ 3 \times (10)$$
$$+ 3$$

Binary is very similar except when we write a binary number we mean that the far right digit represents units, the next left twos, the next left fours (two times twos), the next left eights (two times two times twos), and so on.

(ii) For example:
$$1011 = 1 \times (2 \times 2 \times 2)$$
$$+ 0 \times (2 \times 2)$$
$$+ 1 \times (2)$$
$$+ 1$$

So 1011 in base two is 11 in base ten. Check it.

Fractions can also be represented in binary. To see how, recall what we mean when we write a decimal fraction. We mean that the first digit to the right of the decimal point represents tenths, the next right hundredths (tenths of tenths), the next right thousandths (tenths of tenths of tenths), then ten thousandths, and so on.

(iii) For example:
$$0.5333 = 5 \times (1/10)$$
$$+ 3 \times (1/10 \times 1/10)$$
$$+ 3 \times (1/10 \times 1/10 \times 1/10)$$
$$+ 3 \times (1/10 \times 1/10 \times 1/10 \times 1/10)$$

The pattern must be clear by now. In a binary fraction the first digit to the right of the decimal point represents halves, the next right quarters (halves of halves), the next right eighths (halves of halves of halves), and so on.

(iv) For example:
$$0.1111 = 1 \times (1/2)$$
$$+ 1 \times (1/2 \times 1/2)$$
$$+ 1 \times (1/2 \times 1/2 \times 1/2)$$
$$+ 1 \times (1/2 \times 1/2 \times 1/2 \times 1/2)$$

So 0.1111 in base two is $15/16$ in base ten.

To understand how to count in binary imagine the odometer of an automobile. This records the total mileage traveled – base ten. It usually consists of a row of adjacent wheels turning on a spindle. Each wheel has the digits 0 to 9 around its circumference. When the car moves the rightmost wheel turns. When it reaches 9 and begins to show 0 the wheel on its left is dragged along and made to advance by one notch. In this way a ten is carried to the left hand wheel. Similarly, when the left hand wheel reaches 9 and begins to show 0 the wheel to its left is dragged along and made to advance by one notch. In this way a hundred is carried. And so on. This is the way we count in base ten.

Now consider a binary odometer. If such a device were to exist its wheels would carry only the digits 0 and 1. In a binary odometer whenever a wheel reaches 1 and begins to show 0 the wheel on its left

Below: The use of high-level languages, such as Basic, allows even inexperienced users to communicate with a computer, without ever having to understand binary notation. This is possible because the computer acts as an interpreter.

Below: A digital computer can handle numbers, text, or graphics, but it works in binary. It can accept binary digits stored as levels of magnetism on program disks or, stored temporarily as voltages in Random Access Memory.

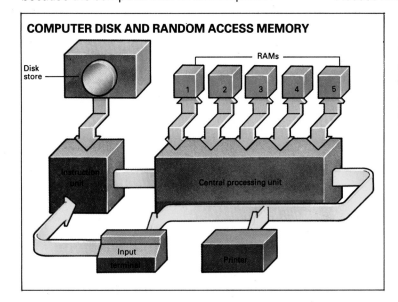

COMPUTER DISK AND RANDOM ACCESS MEMORY

Disk store

RAMs
1 2 3 4 5

Instruction unit

Central processing unit

Input terminal

Printer

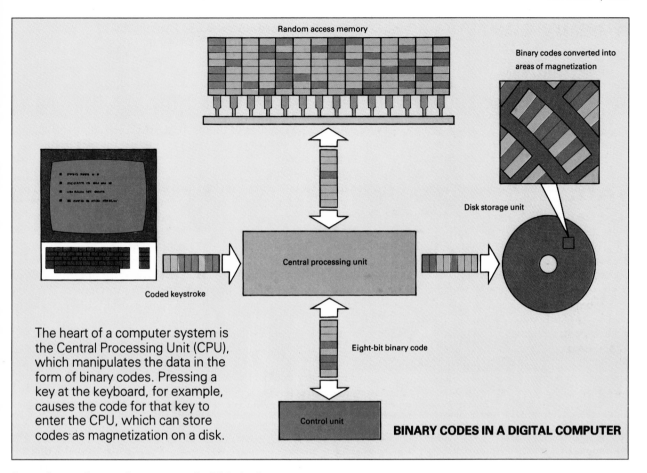

Random access memory

Binary codes converted into
areas of magnetization

Disk storage unit

Central processing unit

Coded keystroke

Eight-bit binary code

Control unit

The heart of a computer system is the Central Processing Unit (CPU), which manipulates the data in the form of binary codes. Pressing a key at the keyboard, for example, causes the code for that key to enter the CPU, which can store codes as magnetization on a disk.

BINARY CODES IN A DIGITAL COMPUTER

is made to advance by one notch. This is the way to count in base two, binary.

(v) Here are some examples of binary arithmetic and beside them the base ten equivalents:

a)
```
  1001      9
+  101    + 5
  ────     ──
  1110     14
```

b)
```
  11101     29
-  1001    - 9
  ─────     ──
  10100     20
```

c)
```
   101      5
×   11    × 3
  ────     ──
  1111     15
```

Converting a binary number to decimal, base ten is just a matter of thinking about what a binary number means. Look back to example (ii) and see how it was done. But converting a decimal number to binary is slightly more tricky. In principal all we have to do is express our decimal number as a sum of units, twos, fours, eights, etc.

For example: $63 = 32 + 16 + 8 + 4 + 2 + 1$

So $63 = 1 \quad 1 \quad 1 \quad 1 \quad 1 \quad 1$ in binary.

But this isn't always easy to do. Fortunately there is a useful trick to help us convert from decimal to binary. Keep dividing your decimal number by two and writing down the remainder.

(vi) Take, for example, the decimal number, 39; r. is the remainder.

```
2 | 39
2 | 19   r.1
2 |  9   r.1
2 |  4   r.1
2 |  2   r.0
2 |  1   r.0
  |  0   r.1
```

Stop dividing by two when there's nothing left and read the remainders from bottom to top. So, in this case 39 in base ten is 100111 in binary.

John von Neumann, the American mathematician, born in Hungary, was the first to realize the advantages of using binary to represent numbers inside a computer. A computer consists of banks of tiny electronic components each of which can be in one of two states: *on*, letting an electric current flow; or *off*, allowing no current to flow. These states can represent the 0 and 1 of a binary digit (a *bit* in computer jargon). Modern-day computers even encode the instructions (*programs* in computer talk) which manipulate and store numbers as strings of binary digits on disks or in the machine's memory.

See also: Artificial intelligence; Computer; Data storage; Mathematics; Memory device.

Binding energy

Binding energy is the energy involved in holding together the component parts of a MOLECULE, an ATOM or a NUCLEUS. It is a term used particularly in connection with the nucleus and is the source of both types of nuclear energy, FISSION and FUSION, which have had such an impact on the modern world.

The realization that large amounts of energy are available from the nuclei of the atoms followed from precise measurements of nuclear masses early this century. In instruments called MASS SPECTROGRAPHS, the masses can be accurately calculated by measuring the curvature of the paths taken by charged clusters of particles as they travel through electric and magnetic fields. The measurements reveal something which, taken by itself, seems impossible. The masses of the nuclei are less than the total arrived at by adding the masses of the protons and neutrons of which they are formed.

This enigma can be resolved only through Einstein's famous formula $E = mc^2$ (ENERGY equals MASS multipled by the speed of light, squared). Mass and energy are interchangeable and the mass which is missing in the sums on the nucleus is related to the energy which holds the nucleus together. This is the binding energy, which was also known initially as the mass defect. Some of the particles' mass has been converted into energy and to separate the original particles, with their higher total mass, energy has to be supplied to the nucleus to break it up.

When the nuclei of all the chemical elements are

Below: The remnants of a supernova explosion. An enormous amount of binding energy is released as the massive star fragments itself.

examined a crucial fact emerges. Most of the elements have nuclei with a binding energy of about 8 MeV or 8 million electron volts per particle – nearly a thousand times the energy of an electron fired by a television picture tube. The lightest and heaviest elements, however, have less binding energy per particle on account of the structure of their nuclei. The amount of mass that is missing when doing the sums on the nucleus is greater for the elements near the center of the PERIODIC TABLE; if the light or heavy elements can be converted into these central elements some mass can be liberated as free energy.

To take a specific example, a helium nucleus is built up of two PROTONS and two NEUTRONS. The mass of a proton (the nucleus of the normal hydrogen atom) is about 1.7 millionth of a millionth of a millionth of a millionth of a gram. This is a rather clumsy unit with which to calculate and, using the mass-energy equivalence, the nuclear physicist usually handles the proton mass in units of energy – a proton is 938 MeV, and neutron is slightly heavier with 939.5 MeV. The helium nucleus is, however, 3727 MeV or 28 MeV less massive than its constituents: 28 MeVs worth of energy can be released in the formation of a single nucleus. Compared with conventional sources, this is a colossal amount of energy.

Conventional energy sources, say the burning of oil, involve atomic binding energies – they are chemical reactions to do with the binding of the electron clouds surrounding the nuclei in atoms and molecules. Here also, the release of energy is connected with the conversion of mass – the products of the burned oil have very slightly less mass than the oil itself – but nuclear energy sources, which bring the center of the atom into play, are several million times more powerful. If all the hydrogen nuclei in a glass of water could be combined to create helium nuclei, enough energy would be liberated to drive an ocean liner across the Atlantic.

This process of joining light elements together to form heavier ones is known as fusion, and it is the process that powers the H (hydrogen) bomb, the Sun and the stars. There is a great deal of research under way in an attempt to master fusion in the laboratory so that it can be used in power plants. The progress has been slow, because, in order to overcome the natural repulsion between positively charged hydrogen nuclei, temperatures as high as ten million degrees must be sustained in a laboratory.

At the other end of the table of elements, the breaking up of heavy nuclei such as uranium is another source of energy. This process is known as fission. A uranium nucleus usually breaks up into two almost equal parts ending up, for example as nuclei of molybdenum and palladium.

See also: Atom and molecule; Fission; Fusion.

Binoculars

A pair of binoculars is essentially two telescopes mounted side by side. Since both eyes are used to look at a scene, a stereoscopic view is obtained so that nearby objects are seen in depth, and there is less eye strain than with a single telescope.

The simplest binocular instrument uses two Galilean telescopes, each of which has just two lenses. Known generally as an opera glass or field glass, this has a rather small field of view – like looking through a tube – and a low magnification, rarely more than four times.

Better telescopes usually have *achromatic lenses* and are much longer and heavier than the Galilean type. To make a powerful pair of binoculars using ordinary telescopes without any modification would mean that they would be very long and clumsy. But by using a pair of right-angled PRISMS in each optical system, the light can be folded so that the distance it travels between the front object glass and the eyepiece is lengthened quite considerably without lengthening the body of the instrument. This also allows the object glasses to be offset so that they can be further apart than the viewer's eyes, giving a greater stereo effect and allowing larger

Above: An operative using a binocular-based Laserguide rangefinder. This is a highly specialized application of binocular vision, but the principle is not unlike the one used on the once popular rangefinder cameras. Below: The light through a binocular is reflected an even number of times so the image is viewed upright, unlike a telescope in which the image is normally viewed upside down.

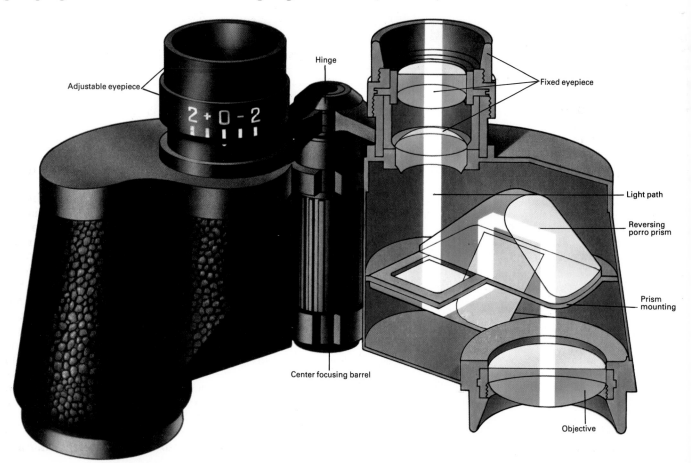

Adjustable eyepiece

Hinge

Fixed eyepiece

Light path

Reversing porro prism

Prism mounting

Center focusing barrel

Objective

LASERGAGE LP7 RANGEFINDER

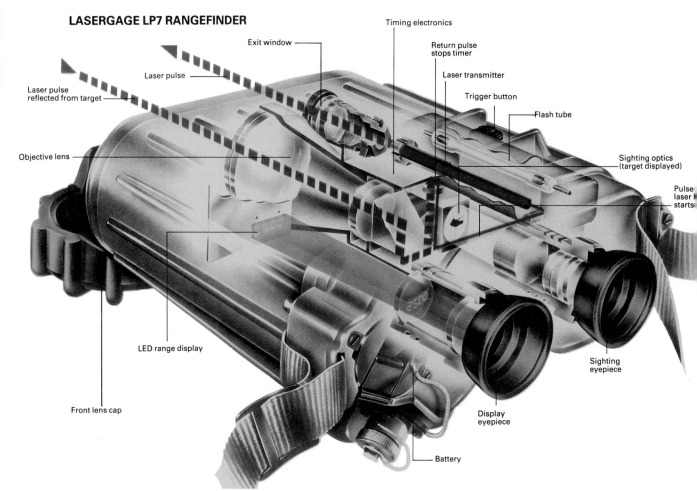

Laser pulse reflected from target

Laser pulse

Exit window

Timing electronics

Return pulse stops timer

Laser transmitter

Trigger button

Flash tube

Objective lens

Sighting optics (target displayed)

Pulse laser starts

LED range display

Sighting eyepiece

Front lens cap

Display eyepiece

Battery

lenses to be used without touching at the center. The basic telescope design gives an upside down image, but the prisms turn it the right way up so no extra lenses need be used.

Focusing is usually carried out by a central wheel on a bridge which links the two eyepiece tubes. Turning this wheel moves the two tubes in or out simultaneously. There are often differences in strength between an individual's eyes, so a separate twist focusing thread is provided on the right hand eyepiece to allow for this. These center focus (CF) models can be quickly focused on objects at different distances, and so are popular. They are not as robust as independent focusing (IF) models, however, in which each eyepiece is fitted directly to the main body and has to be focused separately. Binoculars intended for military or marine use are of the independent focus type.

The two halves of a pair of binoculars are hinged, so that each user can alter them to suit the distance between his eyes. A scale marked on the bridge shows this separation in millimeters. A value of 2.5 in. (64 mm) is common.

If the two light paths of the separate halves of the binocular are not parallel, a double image will be

Above: A binocular laser rangefinder combines the advantages of compactness and ease of use.

seen. Even a slight misalignment is noticeable, if only by the discomfort produced when the eyes try to bring the image together. This is actually bad for the eyes, and binoculars should always be perfectly *collimated* so that the beams are parallel.

The prisms are held in place in recesses by metal straps, and are adjusted to collimate the beam by using wedges or screws. Fine adjustment is carried out by rotating the *cells* which carry the object glasses. These cells are made so that the lens is slightly off center; the screw thread they fit into is also slightly off center so that by turning one inside the other the lens can be brought to any position, including dead center.

Cheap binoculars, though they may at first appear to be every bit as good as more expensive ones, often have poor prism mountings. Usually, the prisms can be knocked out of alignment easily and ruin the instrument.

See also: Achromatic lens; Laser and maser; Lens; Light; Optics; Prism.